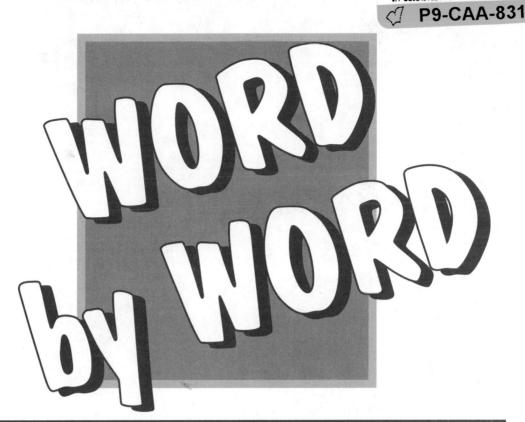

WORD by WORD

Beginning Workbook

Canadian Edition

Steven J. Molinsky · Bill Bliss

Contributing Author
Ann Kennedy

Prentice Hall Allyn and Bacon Canada
Scarborough, Ontario

Canadian Cataloguing in Publication Data

Molinsky, Steven J.
    Word by word: beginning workbook

ISBN 0-13-622374-5

1. Picture dictionaries, English – Problems, exercises,
etc. 2. English language – Textbooks for second language
learners.* I. Bliss, Bill. II. Molinsky, Steven J.
Word by word picture dictionary. III. Title

PE1629.M48 1997 Suppl. 1   423'.1   C97-930083-5

Canadian Adaptation: *Elynor Kagan*
Acquisitions Editor: *Dominique Roberge*
Developmental Editor: *Marta Tomins*
Production Editor: *Mary Ann McCutcheon*
Director of Creative Services: *Jan Coughtrey*
Production Coordinator: *Jane Schell*
Interior Design: *Kenny Beck and Jan Sivertsen*
Cover Design: *Merle Krumper*
Text Formatting: *Steve Lewis*
Illustrations: RICHARD E. HILL

The authors gratefully acknowledge the contribution of Tina Carver
in the development of the *Word by Word* program.

© 1997 Prentice-Hall Canada Inc.
A Division of Simon & Schuster/A Viacom Company
1870 Birchmount Road, Scarborough, Ontario M1P 2J7

Prentice-Hall, Inc., *Upper Saddle River, New Jersey*
Prentice-Hall International (UK) Limited, *London*
Prentice-Hall of Australia, Pty. Limited, *Sydney*
Prentice-Hall Hispanoamericana, S.A., *Mexico City*
Prentice-Hall of India Private Limited, *New Delhi*
Prentice-Hall of Japan, Inc., *Tokyo*
Simon & Schuster Southeast Asia Private Limited, *Singapore*
Editora Prentice-Hall do Brasil, Ltda., *Rio de Janeiro*

ISBN 0-13-622374-5

Original English language edition published by
Prentice Hall Regents, Upper Saddle River, New Jersey
Copyright © 1994

1 2 3 4 5   W   01 00 99 98 97

Printed and bound in Canada

Visit the Prentice Hall Canada Web site!
Send us your comments, browse our catalogues, and more.

www.phcanada.com

Or reach us through e-mail at

phabinfo_pubcanada@prenhall.com

CONTENTS

The *Word by Word* Picture Dictionary presents more than 3000 vocabulary words through lively full-colour illustrations. This innovative Picture Dictionary offers students the essential vocabulary they need to communicate effectively in a wide range of Canadian contexts.

Word by Word organizes the vocabulary into 100 thematic units, providing a careful sequence of lessons that range from the immediate world of the student to the world at large. Early units on the family, the home, and daily activities lead to lessons on the community, school, workplace, shopping, recreation, and other topics relevant to life in Canada. *Word by Word* offers extensive coverage of important lifeskill competencies and the vocabulary of school subjects and extracurricular activities. The Canadian edition features a map of Canada showing provinces, territories, and major cities; Canadian symbols; Canadian currency; metric weights and measures; and Canadian spelling. Since each unit is self-contained, *Word by Word* can be used either sequentially or in any desired order.

For users' convenience, the units in *Word by Word* are listed two ways: sequentially in the Table of Contents, and alphabetically in the Thematic Index. These resources, combined with the Glossary in the appendix, allow students and teachers to quickly and easily locate all words and topics in the Picture Dictionary.

The *Word by Word* Picture Dictionary is the centrepiece of the complete *Word by Word* Vocabulary Development Program, which offers a wide selection of print and media support materials for instruction at all levels. Ancillary materials for the Canadian edition include *Workbooks* at two different levels (*Beginning* and *Intermediate*), and a *Teacher's Resource Book*.

The Beginning and Intermediate Workbooks offer stimulating and motivating reinforcement through reading, writing, and listening comprehension practice. The *Word by Word* Workbooks are designed to work equally well in single- and multi-level classes. All students can work on the same Picture Dictionary lesson while using Workbooks geared to their individual levels.

The original program includes a number of items that can be used selectively to accompany the Canadian editions of the Picture Dictionary and the Workbooks: a Handbook of Vocabulary Teaching Strategies, a complete Audio Program, Wall Charts, Colour Transparencies, Vocabulary Game Cards, a Song Album and accompanying Song Book, and a Testing Program. In the Workbooks, scripts for all units are provided, so that teachers (perhaps with the help of more advanced students) can create audio tapes themselves, or simply read the scripts to the students as they complete the listening activities.

Word by Word aims to offer students a communicative, meaningful, and lively way of practising English vocabulary. In conveying to you the substance of our program, we hope that we have also conveyed the spirit: that learning vocabulary can be genuinely interactive . . . relevant to our students' lives . . . responsive to students' differing strengths and learning styles . . . and fun!

Steven J. Molinsky
Bill Bliss

A. WHAT'S THE WORD?

first	family

1. What's your ____first____ name?
   John.
2. What's your _____ name?
   Thompson.

apartment	social insurance	phone

3. What's your _____ number?
   565-7937.
4. What's your _____ number?
   450 785 785.
5. What's your _____ number?
   312.

postal	area

6. What's your _____ code?
   V6L 3H4.
7. What's your _____ code?
   604.

B. WHAT'S THE ANSWER?

_d_ 1. What's your surname?   **a.** 365 Maple Avenue.
___ 2. What's your first name?   **b.** W-A-T-T-E-R-S-O-N.
___ 3. What's your address?   **c.** Joseph.
___ 4. How do you spell that?   **d.** Watterson.
___ 5. What's your apartment number?   **e.** Vancouver.
___ 6. What's your city?   **f.** 435 685 684.
___ 7. What's your telephone number?   **g.** 690-6949.
___ 8. What's your social insurance number?   **h.** 3B.

C. YOUR APPLICATION

Fill in the form with your personal information.

NAME:	_____	_____	_____
	LAST	FIRST	MIDDLE
ADDRESS:	_____		_____
	NUMBER STREET		APT. #
	_____	_____	_____
	CITY	PROVINCE	POSTAL CODE

A. WHICH GROUP?

wife	husband	mother	father	daughter
son	sister	brother	niece	nephew

- _____wife_____
- _____
- _____
- _____
- _____

- _____
- _____
- _____
- _____
- _____

B. HIS NAME OR HER NAME?

His	Her

1. What's your sister's name?
   ___Her___ name is Ellen.

2. What's your nephew's name?
   _____ name is Bob.

3. What's your daughter's name?
   _____ name is Carolyn.

4. What's your grandson's name?
   _____ name is David.

5. What's your husband's name?
   _____ name is Steven.

6. What's your wife's name?
   _____ name is Mary.

C. WHO IS WHO?

_e_ 1. My sister's daughter is   **a.** my nephew.

___ 2. My mother's father is   **b.** my son.

___ 3. My father's mother is   **c.** my mother.

___ 4. My brother's son is   **d.** my grandmother.

___ 5. My grandfather's daughter is   **e.** my niece.

___ 6. My grandson's father is   **f.** my grandfather.

D. IN OTHER WORDS

Look at page 2 of the Picture Dictionary. Which word means the same?

1. Mom = _____mother_____

2. Dad = _____

3. Grandpa = _____

4. Grandma = _____

A. WHICH GROUP?

Look at page 3 of the Picture Dictionary. Write each word in the correct place in this diagram.

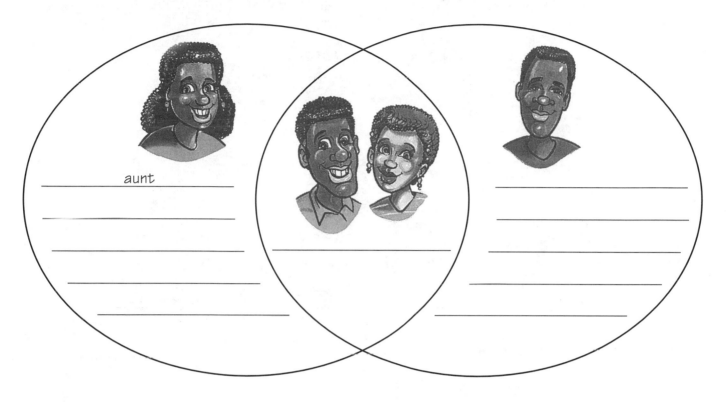

aunt

B. WHICH WORD?

1. She's my (⟨aunt⟩ uncle).
    What's (her   his) name?

2. (She's   He's) my son-in-law.
    Where does (she   he) live?

3. (He   His) name is John.
    Is he your (niece   nephew)?

4. Is she your (niece   nephew)?
    Yes. (Her   His) name is Sally.

5. Is he your (uncle   aunt)?
    No. He's my (cousin   sister-in-law).

6. Is (he   she) your daughter-in-law?
    Yes. Her (husband   father) is my son.

C. WHAT'S THE WORD?

1. Is she your aunt?
    Yes. She's my father's _____sister_____.

2. Is he your grandfather?
    Yes. He's my mother's _____.

3. Is she your mother-in-law?
    Yes. She's my husband's _____.

4. Is he your brother-in-law?
    Yes. He's my husband's _____.

5. Is he your nephew?
    Yes. He's my sister's _____.

6. Is she your niece?
    Yes. She's my brother's _____.

D. AT PAT AND JIM'S WEDDING

Rita and Sam are at Pat and Jim's wedding. Write the correct words to complete the conversation. Then practise the conversation with a friend.

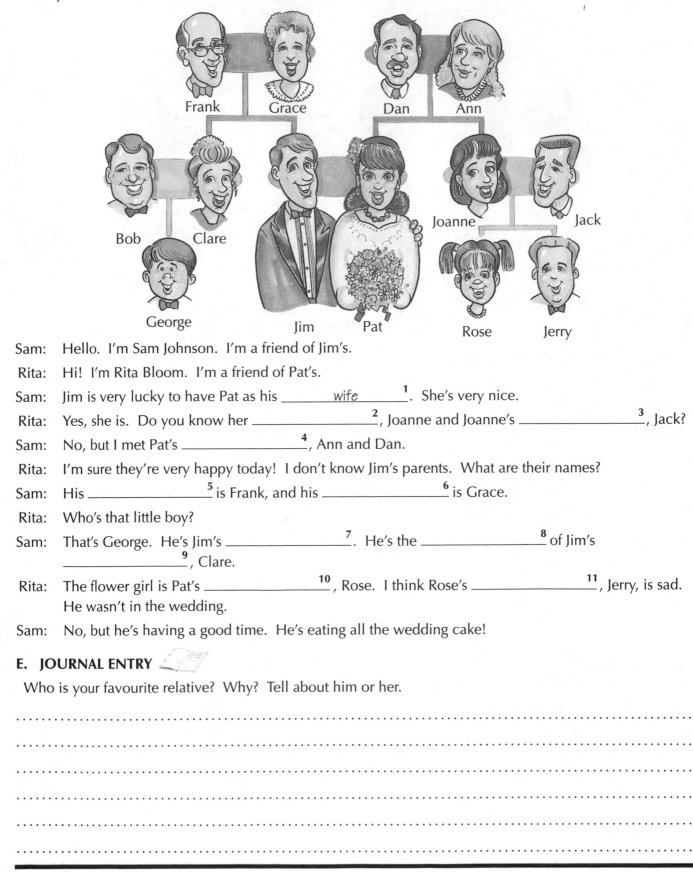

Sam: Hello. I'm Sam Johnson. I'm a friend of Jim's.

Rita: Hi! I'm Rita Bloom. I'm a friend of Pat's.

Sam: Jim is very lucky to have Pat as his _____ wife _____ [1]. She's very nice.

Rita: Yes, she is. Do you know her _____ [2], Joanne and Joanne's _____ [3], Jack?

Sam: No, but I met Pat's _____ [4], Ann and Dan.

Rita: I'm sure they're very happy today! I don't know Jim's parents. What are their names?

Sam: His _____ [5] is Frank, and his _____ [6] is Grace.

Rita: Who's that little boy?

Sam: That's George. He's Jim's _____ [7]. He's the _____ [8] of Jim's _____ [9], Clare.

Rita: The flower girl is Pat's _____ [10], Rose. I think Rose's _____ [11], Jerry, is sad. He wasn't in the wedding.

Sam: No, but he's having a good time. He's eating all the wedding cake!

E. JOURNAL ENTRY

Who is your favourite relative? Why? Tell about him or her.

. . . .

. . . .

. . . .

. . . .

. . . .

. . . .

A. USING A COMPASS

Write each word on the correct line.

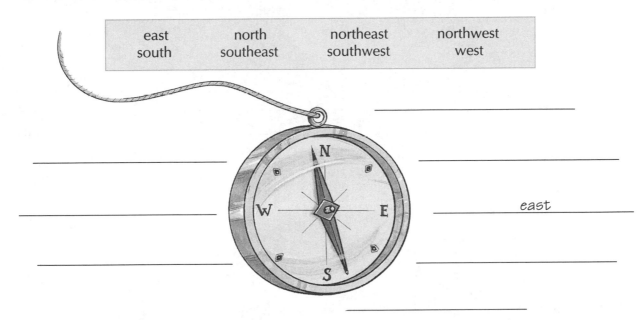

east	north	northeast	northwest
south	southeast	southwest	west

_____

_____   _____

_____   _____ *east* _____

_____   _____

_____

B. USING THE MAP: *CANADA*

_c_ **1.** The Yukon is in the   **a.** northeast.

___ **2.** Ontario is in   **b.** west.

___ **3.** Labrador is in the   **c.** northwest.

___ **4.** Nova Scotia is in the   **d.** central Canada.

___ **5.** British Columbia is in the   **e.** east.

C. WHICH REGION?

Can you name . . .

1. the 4 provinces known as the western provinces?

_____ British Columbia _____   _____

_____   _____

2. the 4 provinces known as the Atlantic provinces?

_____   _____

_____   _____

3. the 2 provinces known as central Canada?

_____   _____

A. WHICH CONTINENT?

Argentina Germany	Austria France	Brazil Japan	Chile Korea	China Nigeria	Egypt Zaire

South America:
- ____Argentina____
- _____
- _____

Europe:
- _____
- _____
- _____

Asia:
- _____
- _____
- _____

Africa:
- _____
- _____
- _____

B. A TRIP AROUND THE WORLD

Indian	Pacific	Atlantic	Arctic	Mediterranean

We're taking a trip around the world . . . by ship! We're leaving from Halifax. First we sail to New York. Then it takes one week to cross the _____Atlantic_____[1] Ocean to get to England. Then we're going south to Portugal. Then we're going through the _____[2] Sea to get to Italy. Then we're going to visit Egypt and go south through the Red Sea, between Egypt and Saudi Arabia. Then we're going to take a long trip through the _____[3] Ocean to Australia. We're then going northeast through the _____[4] Ocean to Hawaii. We don't want to go north to the _____[5] Ocean! It's too cold!

C. JOURNAL ENTRY

What country do you want to visit some day? Why? Where is it?

. . . .

. . . .

. . . .

. . . .

. . . .

. . . .

A. WHAT DO THEY DO?

washes	get	say	takes	shaves	brushes
combs	go	get	have	puts on	makes

Sally and Sam _____ *get* _____ [1] up early every day. He _____ [2]
a shower, _____ [3], and _____ [4] his hair. They _____ [5]
dressed and _____ [6] breakfast. She _____ [7] her teeth,
_____ [8] her face, and _____ [9] makeup. He _____ [10]
the beds. They _____ [11] good-bye and _____ [12] to work.

B. CROSSWORD: *PICTURES AND WORDS*

ACROSS

2.

4.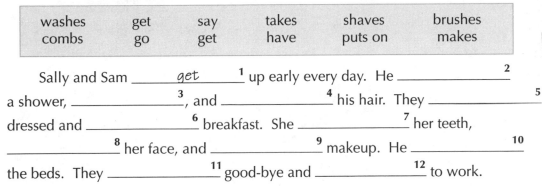

DOWN

1.

3.

(crossword: C O M B across at 2, with 1, 3 down and 4 across)

C. CROSSWORD: *WHAT DO WE DO?*

ACROSS

1. We have . . . .

4. We eat . . . .

DOWN

2. We make the . . . .

3. We take a . . . .

(crossword: B R E A K F A S T across at 1, with 2, 3 down and 4 across)

D. WHAT'S THE SEQUENCE?

Put these actions in the best order.

___	cook dinner
1	get up
___	make breakfast
___	have lunch
___	get dressed
___	go to bed

E. MATCHING

_f_ 1.	get	a.	a bath
___ 2.	put on	b.	my face
___ 3.	wash	c.	the bed
___ 4.	floss	d.	makeup
___ 5.	make	e.	my teeth
___ 6.	take	f.	undressed

A. WHICH WORD?

1. She's vacuuming the (cat (floor)).
2. Are you going to wash the (dishes   TV)?
3. I'm going to dust the (piano   music).
4. He's going to (exercise   play) the piano.
5. I'm going to (iron   do) now.

6. I'm going to feed the (dog   laundry).
7. Are you going to sweep the (floor   baby)?
8. I'm listening to the (radio   basketball).
9. She's going to watch (the radio   TV).
10. Are you cleaning the (laundry   house)?

B. MATCHING

_d_ 1. walk the dog
___ 2. wash the dishes
___ 3. sweep the floor
___ 4. feed the dog
___ 5. study
___ 6. play the guitar

a. give the dog something to eat
b. clean plates, cups, and glasses
c. use a broom
d. take a walk with the dog
e. make music
f. get ready for a test

C. WHAT'S THE ACTION?

feed	do	iron	watch	listen to	play	read

listen to
- radio
- music

_____
- laundry
- homework

_____
- shirts
- dresses

_____
- television
- basketball game

_____
- cat
- dog
- baby

_____
- books
- newspapers
- textbooks

_____
- basketball
- guitar
- piano

D. LISTENING: *WHAT ARE THEY DOING?*

Listen and choose the correct answer.

1. a. He's feeding the cat.
   (b.) He's feeding the baby.
2. a. She's washing the dishes.
   b. She's walking the dog.
3. a. He's playing basketball.
   b. He's playing the guitar.

4. a. She's studying.
   b. She's dusting.
5. a. He's ironing.
   b. He's exercising.
6. a. She's sweeping the floor.
   b. She's watching TV.

A. WHERE ARE THE THINGS?

Look at page 10 of the Picture Dictionary. Write the correct word.

1. There's a <u>g l o b e</u> next to the pencil sharpener.

2. There's an _ _ _ _ _ _ _ _ projector on the bookshelf.

3. There's a _ _ _ _ _ _ next to the flag.

4. There's an _ _ _ _ _ _ next to the chalk on the chalk tray.

5. There's a _ _ _ _ _ _ _ _ _ _ _ on the girl's desk.

6. There's a _ _ _ _ _ next to the calculator on the girl's desk.

B. MATCHING

<u>f</u> **1.** chalk   **a.** paper

___ **2.** teaching   **b.** screen

___ **3.** graph   **c.** board

___ **4.** movie   **d.** projector

___ **5.** bulletin   **e.** assistant

___ **6.** slide   **f.** tray

C. MATCHING: *COMPOUND WORDS*

Draw a line to complete the word. Then write the word on the line.

1. text   speaker   <u>textbook</u>

2. loud   tack   _____

3. thumb   shelf   _____

4. book   book   _____

D. HOW DO WE USE THEM?

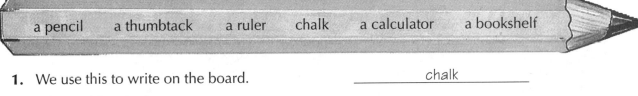

a pencil   a thumbtack   a ruler   chalk   a calculator   a bookshelf

1. We use this to write on the board.   <u>chalk</u>

2. We use this to write on paper.   _____

3. We use this to keep books on.   _____

4. We use this to put papers on a bulletin board.   _____

5. We use this to draw straight lines.   _____

6. We use this to add and subtract numbers.   _____

E. CHECK-OFF LIST

What do you have? What does your classroom have? Put a check next to the items.

I have:

___ pen
___ pencil
___ eraser
___ notebook
___ graph paper
___ ruler
___ calculator

My classroom has:

___ flag   ___ bulletin board
___ clock   ___ P. A. system
___ board   ___ map
___ chalk   ___ pencil sharpener
___ globe   ___ computer
___ eraser   ___ bookshelf

A. THE TEACHER'S INSTRUCTIONS

1. Raise your (seat (hand)).
2. Erase your (mistake   book).
3. Write your (homework   projector).
4. Go over your (test   board).
5. Pass out the (projectors   papers).
6. Lower (the shade   up).
7. Listen to (the answer   your seat).
8. Erase the (question   hand).
9. Study in (groups   lights).
10. Turn on (the page   the light).

B. WHAT'S THE SEQUENCE?

Put these actions in the best order.

___ Correct your mistakes.

___ Write your name.

___ Check your answers.

___ Hand in your test.

_1_ Take out a piece of paper.

___ Answer the questions.

C. WHAT ARE THEY DOING?

Write a sentence about each classroom action.

1. _____ She's writing her name.

2. _____

3. _____

4. _____

5. _____

6. _____

COUNTRIES, NATIONALITIES, AND LANGUAGES

A. LANGUAGES AND COUNTRIES

1. Name 5 countries where the people speak English:

_____England_____   _____   _____

_____   _____

2. Name 5 countries where the people speak Spanish:

_____   _____   _____

_____   _____

3. Name 3 countries where the people speak Arabic:

_____   _____   _____

4. Name 2 countries where the people speak Portuguese:

_____   _____

B. COUNTRY, NATIONALITY, OR LANGUAGE?

1. What's your native language?

I speak (Saudi (Arabic)).

2. Where are you going on your vacation?

We're going to (Argentina   Argentine).

3. What country are you from?

I'm from (France   French).

4. What's your nationality?

I'm (Taiwan   Taiwanese).

5. Where are you from?

We're from (Poland   Polish).

6. Do you speak Cambodian?

No. I speak (Vietnam   Vietnamese).

7. Who is she?

She's my cousin from (Honduras   Honduran).

8. What's your nationality?

I'm (Jordanian   Jordan).

9. What language do you speak?

I speak (Romania   Romanian).

10. What languages do you speak?

English and (Japan   Japanese).

C. WHAT'S THE WORD?

Our English class has many students from many different countries. Paola is from Italy. She speaks _____Italian_____[1]. Gilberto is Brazilian. He speaks _____[2]. Alicja and Waldek are from _____[3]. They speak Polish. Erdal, from Turkey, speaks _____[4]. Karl is _____[5] and he speaks Latvian. Haija and Sun Hee are _____[6] and speak Korean. Angela is Venezuelan and Adriana is Colombian. They both speak _____[7]. There are many students and many languages, but everyone in our English class has one language that everyone understands: _____![8]

A. MATCHING

_f_ 1. A private home is

___ 2. There are many apartments in

___ 3. College students often live in

___ 4. A special place for older people is

___ 5. A house on water is

___ 6. A small house in the mountains is

a. a residence.

b. a cabin.

c. an apartment building.

d. a houseboat.

e. a nursing home.

f. a single-family house.

B. LISTENING: *CALLING FOR A TAXI*

Listen to the conversation. Write the number next to the correct words.

___ residence ___ townhouse ___ mobile home ___ nursing home __1__ house

C. CROSSWORD

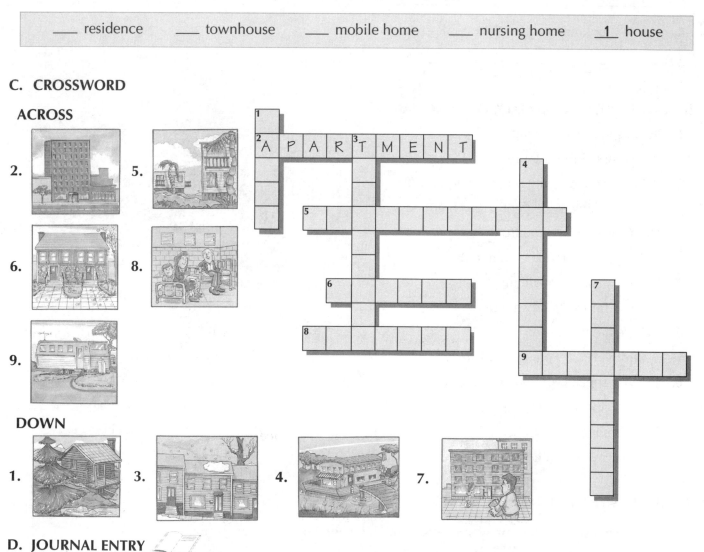

ACROSS

2.

5.

6.

8.

9.

DOWN

1.

3.

4.

7.

APARTMENT

D. JOURNAL ENTRY

What type of housing do you live in now? Describe it.

....

....

....

....

A. MAKING LISTS

List 3 things you can sit on:

- _____armchair_____
- _____
- _____

List 4 things you can plug in:

- _____
- _____
- _____
- _____

B. WHERE IS IT?

Look at page 14 of the Picture Dictionary. Write the correct word.

1. There's a t e l e v i s i o n in the entertainment unit.
2. There's a _ _ _ _ _ on the end table.
3. There are _ _ _ _ _ _ _ on the windows.
4. There's a _ _ _ _ _ _ _ _ _ _ _ _ on the bookcase.
5. There's a _ _ _ _ _ _ _ on the sofa.
6. There's a _ _ _ _ _ _ behind the loveseat.
7. There's a _ _ _ _ _ _ _ _ next to the loveseat.

C. ANALOGIES

couch	end table	fireplace	floor	video cassette recorder	wall unit

1. painting : wall *as* rug : _____floor_____
2. drapes : window *as* screen : _____
3. sofa : loveseat *as* coffee table : _____
4. books : bookcase *as* television : _____
5. drapes : curtains *as* sofa : _____
6. TV : television *as* VCR : _____

D. JOURNAL ENTRY

Imagine you are the cat in the picture on page 14. How do you feel? What are you thinking?

A. MAKING LISTS

List 6 things on the table:
- ___candlestick___
- _____
- _____
- _____
- _____
- _____

List 4 things on the buffet:
- _____
- _____
- _____
- _____

List 4 things on the serving cart:
- _____
- _____
- _____
- _____

B. MATCHING

_f_ **1.** sugar   **a.** pot
___ **2.** coffee   **b.** cabinet
___ **3.** serving   **c.** shaker
___ **4.** salt   **d.** dish
___ **5.** butter   **e.** cart
___ **6.** china   **f.** bowl

C. MATCHING: *COMPOUND WORDS*

Draw a line to complete the word. Then write the word on the line.

1. tea   stick   ___teapot___
2. table   pot   _____
3. centre   cloth   _____
4. candle   piece   _____

D. WHICH WORD DOESN'T BELONG?

1. pitcher   (candle)   coffee pot   teapot
2. sugar bowl   china cabinet   buffet   table
3. centrepiece   salt shaker   butter dish   chandelier
4. tablecloth   coffee pot   creamer   sugar bowl
5. table   serving bowl   chair   china cabinet
6. lamp   table   chandelier   candle

E. LISTENING: *WHAT DO THEY NEED?*

Listen to the conversation. Write the number next to the correct words.

___ teapot   ___ coffee pot   _1_ pitcher   ___ butter dish   ___ sugar bowl

A. ON THE TABLE

Look at page 16 of the Picture Dictionary. Write the correct word.

1. The _____wine glass_____ is between the water glass and the cup.
2. The _____ is between the knife and the soup spoon.
3. The _____ is to the left of the teaspoon.
4. The _____ is under the salad fork and the dinner fork.
5. The _____ is on the bread-and-butter plate.
6. The _____ is between the salad fork and the dinner plate.
7. The _____ is under the salad plate.
8. The _____ is to the right of the teaspoon.

B. WHICH WORD?

1. Oops! I dropped my salad (knife (fork)).
2. This soup (bowl   plate) is very pretty.
3. I'll get a butter (spoon   knife) from the kitchen.
4. I'm sorry I broke the water (napkin   glass).
5. Please get out the cups and (saucers   bowls) so we can serve coffee.
6. Put the (napkin   dinner plate) under the forks.

C. YOUR PLACE SETTING

How do you set a table at home? Draw your place setting below.

Now describe your place setting. Use *on, between, to the right of, to the left of.*

....

....

....

....

....

....

A. THINGS FOR THE BEDROOM

Look at page 17 of the Picture Dictionary. Write the correct word.

1. There's a _____headboard_____ at the head of the bed.

2. There's a _____ on the pillow.

3. There's an _____ blanket on the bed.

4. There's an _____ on the nightstand to the left of the bed.

5. There's a _____ above the dresser.

6. There's a _____ on the bureau.

7. There's a _____ on the night table to the right of the bed.

8. There are _____ on the windows.

B. WHICH WORD DOESN'T BELONG?

1.	blanket	quilt	bedspread	(cot)
2.	blinds	headboard	box spring	footboard
3.	pillowcase	clock radio	fitted sheet	flat sheet
4.	bunk	mirror	trundle	sofa
5.	cot	day bed	twin bed	king-size bed
6.	comforter	mirror	quilt	blanket
7.	fitted sheet	flat sheet	jewelry box	pillowcase

C. *MAKE THE BED!*

Number these items as they appear on a bed, from top (1) to bottom (6).

____ fitted sheet
____ mattress
_1_ bedspread
____ box spring
____ flat sheet
____ blanket

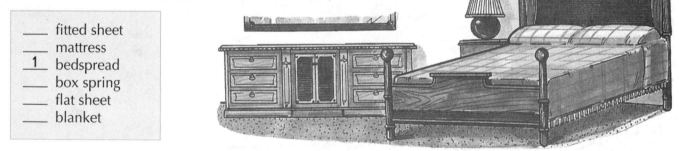

D. LISTENING: *WHAT IS IT?*

Listen to the conversation about beds. Write the number under the correct picture.

____   ____   ____   ____   _1_

A. WHERE ARE THEY?

Look at page 18 of the Picture Dictionary. Write the correct word.

1. There are two _____ placemats _____ on the kitchen table.

2. The _____ is on the kitchen counter in front of the canisters.

3. There's a _____ on the refrigerator door.

4. The _____ is above the dish rack.

5. The _____ is on the kitchen counter to the left of the can opener.

6. There's a _____ above the stove.

7. The _____ is on the kitchen counter next to the refrigerator.

8. The _____ is below the spice rack.

B. MATCHING

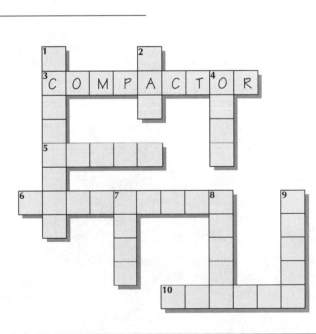

_c_ 1. An ice tray

___ 2. A microwave

___ 3. A refrigerator

___ 4. Dishwashing liquid

___ 5. A refrigerator magnet

___ 6. A cabinet

___ 7. An oven

a. is soap for cleaning dishes.

b. holds plates, cups, and glasses.

c. makes ice cubes for cold drinks.

d. heats food very quickly.

e. bakes food.

f. holds messages to the refrigerator door.

g. keeps food cold.

C. MATCHING: COMPOUND WORDS

Draw a line to complete the word. Then write the word on the line.

1. cook   holder   _____ cookbook _____

2. pot   mat   _____

3. place   washer   _____

4. dish   book   _____

D. CROSSWORD

ACROSS

3. garbage . . . .
5. cutting . . . .
6. dishwasher . . . .
10. paper towel . . . .

DOWN

1. pot . . . .
2. scouring . . . .
4. microwave . . . .
7. spice . . . .
8. dish . . . .
9. ice . . . .

3. C O M P A C T O R

A. MAKING A LIST

List all of the electrical appliances on page 19 of the Picture Dictionary.

_____   _____   _____

_____   _____   _____

_____   _____   _____

_____   _____

B. WHAT'S THE WORD?

1. We use a _____*coffee*_____ _____*grinder*_____ to grind coffee.

2. We use a _____ _____ to make popcorn.

3. We use a _____ _____ to open bottles.

4. We use a _____ _____ to open cans.

5. We use an _____ _____ to beat eggs.

6. We use a _____ _____ to peel vegetables.

C. WHICH WORD?

1. It's taking a long time to cut up these onions.

    You need a (cookie cutter (food processor)).

2. I don't like to cut up garlic in little pieces.

    Use this (vegetable peeler   garlic press).

3. Do you want some tea?

    Yes. I'll put the (ladle   kettle) on the stove.

4. This strainer is very small. Do you have something bigger?

    Try this (colander   rolling pin).

5. This soda is hard to open!

    Here. Use this (bottle opener   paring knife).

D. MATCHING: *ASSOCIATIONS*

_d_ **1.** rolling pin   **a.** cheese

___ **2.** grater   **b.** soup

___ **3.** ladle   **c.** ice cream

___ **4.** peeler   **d.** pies

___ **5.** scoop   **e.** potatoes

A. MATCHING: ASSOCIATIONS

<u>b</u> **1.** crib   **a.** eating

___ **2.** intercom   **b.** sleeping

___ **3.** teddy bear   **c.** playing

___ **4.** stroller   **d.** listening

___ **5.** food warmer   **e.** riding

B. WHICH WORD?

1. Is the baby sleeping?

Yes. He's in his ((cradle) intercom).

2. I'm looking for the baby's toy.

Here's her (night light   doll).

3. It's time to eat!

I'll get the baby's (car seat   high chair).

4. What's that noise?

It's the baby's (chest   rattle).

5. What will the baby sleep in?

Her (potty   portable crib).

6. Where should I put this diaper?

In the (playpen   diaper pail).

7. Where is the baby's stuffed animal?

Look in the (toy chest   mobile).

8. Let's take a walk!

Good idea! Put the baby in the
(booster seat   baby carrier).

C. WHICH WORD DOESN'T BELONG?

1. walker	(mobile)	stroller	carriage
2. crib	doll	rattle	teddy bear
3. playpen	crib	cradle	diaper pail
4. swing	car seat	booster seat	stretch suit
5. stuffed animal	toy chest	crib toy	doll
6. potty	high chair	intercom	baby seat

D. MATCHING

<u>c</u> **1.** change   **a.** light

___ **2.** teddy   **b.** chair

___ **3.** crib   **c.** table

___ **4.** night   **d.** pail

___ **5.** stretch   **e.** chest

___ **6.** diaper   **f.** crib

___ **7.** toy   **g.** warmer

___ **8.** high   **h.** bumper

___ **9.** portable   **i.** suit

___ **10.** food   **j.** bear

A. WHICH WORD?

1. You can wash the baby's hair with this ((shampoo)   food).
2. Give the baby her (diaper pins   vitamins).
3. I have to wash the (formula   teething ring).
4. The baby is crying. Please give him his (soother   ointment).
5. She doesn't like milk. She drinks (baby lotion   formula).
6. Please throw those (cloth   disposable) diapers in the garbage!
7. I always clean my baby's ears with (cotton swabs   baby wipes).
8. She's a messy eater! Put this (powder   bib) on her before you feed her.
9. He's getting a new tooth. Give him his (teething ring   baby shampoo).
10. We need to buy a new (food   nipple) for this bottle.

B. LISTENING: *WHAT ARE THEY TALKING ABOUT?*

1. (liquid vitamins)   baby wipes
2. diaper pins   teething ring
3. baby wipes   cotton swabs
4. disposable diapers   liquid vitamins
5. powder   formula
6. bottle   soother

C. CROSSWORD: *PICTURES TO WORDS*

ACROSS

DOWN

THE BATHROOM

A. WHERE ARE THEY?

Look at the picture on page 22 of the Picture Dictionary. Write the correct word.

1. The h a m p e r is next to the towel rack.

2. The hair dryer is on the _ _ _ _ _ .

3. The shower _ _ _ _ _ _ _ is on the shower curtain rod.

4. The _ _ _ _ _ _ _ is over the sink.

5. A _ _ _ _ _ _ _ _ _ _ _ _ is in the toothbrush holder.

6. The _ _ _ _ _ _ _ _ is next to the toilet.

7. The _ _ _ is next to the sink.

B. MATCHING

_e_ 1. hair   **a.** holder   ___ **6.** toilet   **f.** rug

___ 2. shower   **b.** mat   ___ **7.** air   **g.** rack

___ 3. toothbrush   **c.** towel   ___ **8.** medicine   **h.** freshener

___ 4. hand   **d.** curtain   ___ **9.** bath   **i.** paper

___ 5. rubber   **e.** dryer   ___ **10.** towel   **j.** cabinet

C. WHICH WORD?

1. Clean the tub with this ((sponge)   drain).

2. Put these clothes in the (fan   hamper).

3. Wash your face with (plunger   soap).

4. Put the towel on the (rack   drain).

5. Throw this diaper in the (toilet   wastebasket).

6. How do I turn on the (fan   soap dispenser)?

7. Don't forget to close the (shower curtain   bathtub).

8. Please put the toilet (seat   tank) down.

9. Check your weight with the bathroom (sink   scale).

10. I'm going to take a (bathtub   shower) now.

D. THINGS IN THE BATHROOM

Change one letter to write something you find in the bathroom.

1. van   f a n   4. shell   _ _ _ _ _

2. cut   _ _ _   5. train   _ _ _ _ _

3. soup   _ _ _ _   6. pink   _ _ _ _

A. MATCHING: *ASSOCIATIONS*

_c_ **1.** emery board
___ **2.** comb
___ **3.** toothbrush
___ **4.** tweezers
___ **5.** mascara
___ **6.** blush

a. hair
b. eyebrows
c. fingernails
d. eyelashes
e. cheeks
f. teeth

B. MATCHING: *HOW DO WE USE THEM?*

_c_ **1.** dental floss
___ **2.** shoe polish
___ **3.** shampoo
___ **4.** razor
___ **5.** nail clipper
___ **6.** barrettes

a. to shine shoes
b. to wash hair
c. to clean between teeth
d. to cut fingernails and toenails
e. to keep hair neat
f. for shaving

C. WHICH WORD DOESN'T BELONG?

1. perfume	cologne	(mascara)	deodorant
2. shampoo	shower cap	rinse	conditioner
3. bobby pins	nail polish	hair clips	barrettes
4. mouthwash	hairspray	toothpaste	dental floss
5. tweezers	lipstick	blush	eye shadow
6. emery board	shoe polish	nail polish	nail brush

D. LISTENING: *WHAT ARE THEY TALKING ABOUT?*

Listen to the commercials. What products are they describing? Check the correct answers.

1. ✔ dental floss
___ toothbrush

2. ___ electric razor
___ hairspray

3. ___ nail polish
___ shoe polish

4. ___ hair clips
___ shampoo

5. ___ lipstick
___ mouthwash

6. ___ air freshener
___ hair dryer

7. ___ blush
___ brush

8. ___ hand lotion
___ foundation

9. ___ deodorant
___ styptic pencil

HOUSEHOLD CLEANING AND LAUNDRY

A. WHAT ARE THEY?

Look at page 24 of the Picture Dictionary. Write the correct word.

1. The <u>h a n g e r</u> is over the sink.

2. The _ _ _ _ _ _ _ _ is between the whisk broom and the broom.

3. The _ _ _ _ _ _ _ _ _ bin is on the floor next to the garbage can.

4. The _ _ _ _ _ is on the shelf above the ironing board.

5. The _ _ _ _ _ _ is next to the washing machine.

6. The _ _ _ _ _ _ _ is between the fabric softener and the starch.

7. The _ _ _ _ _ _ _ is in the pail next to the scrub brush.

8. The _ _ _ _ _ _ _ _ _ _ _ are on the clothesline.

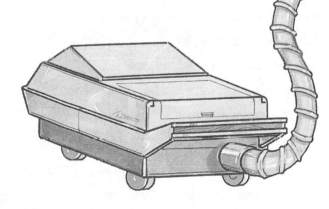

B. WHICH WORD?

1. There's powder all over the bathroom!
   I'll get the (iron (vacuum)).

2. There's water all over the floor!
   Use this (sponge mop   floor wax).

3. I'll do the laundry.
   Here's the (recycling bin   fabric softener).

4. My clothes are still wet!
   Put them back in the (dryer   dustpan).

5. The dryer isn't working.
   That's okay. Use the (dry mop   clothesline).

6. I can't get these clothes white!
   Did you use (ammonia   bleach)?

7. Did you iron your dress?
   Yes. Now I need a (broom   hanger).

8. Where should I throw this away?
   In the (vacuum cleaner   garbage can) in the corner.

C. MATCHING

<u>d</u> 1. furniture   **a.** basket

___ 2. fabric   **b.** sweeper

___ 3. laundry   **c.** towels

___ 4. washing   **d.** polish

___ 5. carpet   **e.** softener

___ 6. dust   **f.** duster

___ 7. feather   **g.** cloth

___ 8. paper   **h.** machine

D. WHICH WORD DOESN'T BELONG?

1.	broom	mop	sweeper	(hanger)
2.	sponge	bin	can	basket
3.	washer	dryer	starch	vacuum
4.	trash can	floor wax	recycling bin	garbage can
5.	cleanser	detergent	bleach	iron
6.	feather duster	laundry bag	whisk broom	dry mop

A. HOME REPAIRS

| satellite | doorknob | screens | lamppost | lawn chair |
| antenna | roof | lawnmower | patio | back |

I had a busy weekend. The television didn't work, so I went on the _____roof_____ [1] and checked the TV _____ [2] and the _____ [3] dish. There was no light on the front walk, so I repaired the _____ [4]. The _____ [5] door didn't open, so I repaired the _____ [6]. I put _____ [7] in all the windows. I fixed the _____ [8] and then cut the grass with it. After all that work, I wanted to relax, so I repaired the _____ [9] and fell asleep in it on the _____ [10].

B. MATCHING: *ASSOCIATIONS*

_c_ **1.** antenna   **a.** light
___ **2.** mailbox   **b.** grass
___ **3.** lamppost   **c.** roof
___ **4.** lawnmower   **d.** letters

___ **5.** garage   **e.** fireplace
___ **6.** satellite dish   **f.** rain
___ **7.** chimney   **g.** television
___ **8.** eavestrough   **h.** car

C. CROSSWORD

Finish the sentences with one word.

ACROSS

2. Rain leaves the roof through the _____.
4. We cook outside on a _____.
6. We open doors by turning the _____.
7. The TV receives signals through the _____.
8. The letter carrier puts letters in the _____.

DOWN

1. Smoke from the fireplace goes up the _____.
3. The machine that cuts the grass is a _____.
5. Don't knock. Ring the _____.

Crossword 2 Across: D R A I N P I P E

D. JOURNAL ENTRY

Describe a typical home in your country. How is it different from the home on page 25?

. . . .

. . . .

. . . .

A. MY APARTMENT BUILDING

elevator	swimming pool	chute	laundry	intercom	doorman
detector	mailboxes	lock	room	peephole	lot

I live in a nice apartment building. In the lobby, there's a _____ *doorman* _____ [1] who
opens the door. When my friends come, they can call me on the _____ [2]. The
_____ [3] are also in the lobby. To come upstairs to my apartment, you can walk
up the stairs, or you can take the _____ [4].

There are other nice things about my apartment building. On every floor, there's a garbage
_____ [5], a _____ [6] room, and a storage _____ [7].
And outdoors there's a large parking _____ [8] and a big _____ [9]!

The apartments are safe. Every door has a dead-bolt _____ [10] and a
_____ [11]. In case of fire, every apartment has a smoke _____ [12].

I like my apartment very much!

B. MATCHING: *COMPOUND WORDS*

Draw a line to the correct word. Then write the new word on the line.

1. peep   man   _____ *peephole* _____
2. door   pool   _____
3. mail   hole   _____
4. whirl   box   _____

C. WHICH WORD?

1. When you visit friends at their house, you ring the (buzzer   (doorbell)).
2. When you visit friends at their apartment, you enter the lobby
   and push the (buzzer   doorbell).
3. When you park outside, you park in a parking (lot   garage).
4. When there's a fire, pull the (smoke detector   fire alarm).
5. Throw the garbage in the (storage room   garbage chute).
6. Leave these boxes in the (storage room   garbage chute).
7. When it gets hot in your apartment, turn on the (air conditioner   smoke detector).
8. To see someone at your door, look through the (intercom   peephole).

D. JOURNAL ENTRY

Describe a typical apartment building in your country. How is it different from the apartment building on page 26?

....

....

....

A. REPAIR AND SERVICE PEOPLE

| painter | locksmith | gardener | carpenter | plumber | exterminator |

1. _____locksmith_____
- doors
- car doors
- garage doors

2. _____
- tap
- toilet
- garbage disposal

3. _____
- flowers
- vegetables

4. _____
- shutters
- wooden steps
- bookcase

5. _____
- ants
- spiders
- mice

6. _____
- walls
- houses
- ceilings

B. HELP!

1. I have mice in my kitchen! Do you know a good _____exterminator_____?
2. My drain isn't working. I need a good _____.
3. I have to use the washer. When is the _____ coming?
4. The lights don't work upstairs. I have to call the _____.
5. Call the _____! All our flowers are dying!
6. The fireplace isn't working. Call the _____.
7. When is the _____ going to come? These walls look terrible!
8. My father can do everything around the house. He's a real _____!

C. MATCHING

_e_ **1.** house
___ **2.** water
___ **3.** repair
___ **4.** chimney
___ **5.** parking
___ **6.** mortgage

a. person
b. bill
c. payment
d. fee
e. painter
f. sweep

D. WHAT KIND OF BILLS ARE THESE?

CCI   GE SMITH   Sept. 20, 1999
           Acct 212 586 9785

Charges through Sept 10
$4.43   Long Distance Calls
  .64   Directory Assistance
16.54   Monthly Service
 1.72   Provincial Tax
 1.51   GST | $24.84 Total |

1. _____ telephone bill _____

City Utilities

Rates for Water/1000 Litres	Consumption thousand litres	Amounts water
1.36	20	27.20

AMOUNT DUE NOW: $27.20

2. _____

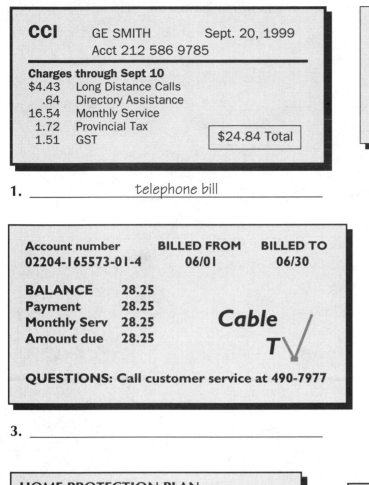

Account number	BILLED FROM	BILLED TO
02204-165573-01-4	06/01	06/30

BALANCE   28.25
Payment   28.25
Monthly Serv   28.25
Amount due   28.25

Cable TV ✓

QUESTIONS: Call customer service at 490-7977

3. _____

Customer Bill

MAR 4 95 Bill for: Please Pay:
456 Queen St. $ 62.15
Calgary, AB

METER READINGS		KILOWATT HOUR USAGE	SUMMARY OF CHARGES	
Mar 2	Jan 31		Description	Amount
12650	01990	660	Residential	62.15

FUEL CHARGE	FUEL CHARGE
c/KWHR 1.418	over 800 4.608

Thank you for your last payment—Use Energy Wisely

4. _____

HOME PROTECTION PLAN

DATE	CHARGES	CREDITS	BALANCE
11/19	55.00	0.00	55.00

Explanation: Termite, cockroach, spider extermination

ACCOUNT NO. 21-68495

PLEASE INCLUDE ACCOUNT NUMBER ON ALL CHECKS.

5. _____

Canadian Home Finance Company Toronto, ON	PAYMENT #45
	Due Sep 15
M/M John McKinley 345 Union Street Toronto, ON M4J 2K3	
PAYMENT #45 in the amount of $1,231.50 Due Sept. 15	$1,231.50

6. _____

Northern Gas Company

Meter Reading	Consumption
13222 from 13050	172m³

FOR COMFORT, SAVINGS, AND CONVENIENCE . . .
                        NATURAL GAS.

AMOUNT DUE NOW: $35.35

7. _____

Canada Wide Oil Company

Oil Used   52 litres
Amount due: $82.45

Want to level off these winter heating bills? Use our budget plan. Call for information.

8. _____

A. HOW ARE THEY USED?

Look at page 28 of the Picture Dictionary. List some of the tools and supplies that are used to . . .

cut	paint	fasten things together
• ___hacksaw___	• _____	• _____
• _____	• _____	• _____
• _____	• _____	• _____
• _____	• _____	• _____

B. WHICH TOOLS?

1. Where's the ((hammer)   chisel)? I have to bang in this nail.
2. Give me that (bit   wire) please. I have to drill a hole.
3. I'm going to clean the paintbrushes with the (washer   paint thinner).
4. Before you paint, smooth the wood with the (hacksaw   sandpaper).
5. I'm cutting wood for the fireplace with this (hatchet   vise).
6. Do we have enough (saw   paint) to finish the walls?
7. Careful! That (power saw   bolt) cuts quickly!
8. You can pull that nail out with the (brace   pliers).

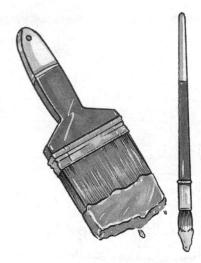

C. WHICH WORD DOESN'T BELONG?

1.	hammer	wrench	(toolbox)	screwdriver
2.	saw	nut	bolt	screw
3.	brush	pan	roller	pliers
4.	hacksaw	saw	screw	hatchet
5.	hammer	hand drill	electric drill	sandpaper
6.	wire	wrench	monkey wrench	pliers

D. LISTENING: *WHAT ARE THEY TALKING ABOUT?*

Listen to the conversation. Circle the correct word.

1.	hammer	(hand drill)	4.	bit	nut	7.	saw	washer
2.	screw	screwdriver	5.	wire	vise	8.	level	chisel
3.	paint thinner	paintbrush	6.	brace	scraper	9.	hacksaw	hatchet

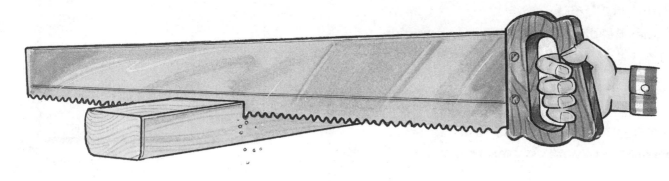

A. WHICH WORD?

1. We have mice! We need a ((mousetrap)   roach killer) right away!

2. We have a problem with the toilet. Where's the (shovel   plunger)?

3. There's ice on the front walk. Let's put down some (fertilizer   sidewalk salt).

4. I can fix that piece of wood with this (oil   glue).

5. I'm going to plant the (grass seed   vegetable seeds) in the garden.

6. Do you have a (sprinkler   flashlight)? It's dark in here and I can't see a thing!

7. This lamp needs (an extension cord   a garden hose).

8. He's cutting the grass with his new (hoe   lawnmower).

9. We had a heavy snowfall last night. I'm going to clear the sidewalk with the (snow shovel   rake).

10. Hand me that (plunger   fly swatter). I'm going to get that pest!

B. MATCHING: SENTENCES

_c_ 1. Where's the hose?   a. I need to measure the floor.

___ 2. Could I borrow your lawnmower?   b. I saw a mouse in the kitchen.

___ 3. I need the flashlight.   c. I have to water the grass.

___ 4. Do we have any mousetraps?   d. I need to cut the grass.

___ 5. Where's the tape measure?   e. I have to paint the ceiling.

___ 6. I need the rake.   f. I have to cut those bushes back.

___ 7. Could I use your step ladder?   g. I have to clean up those leaves.

___ 8. Do we have hedge clippers?   h. I can't see in the dark.

C. MATCHING

_e_ 1. tape   a. ladder   ___ 6. garden   f. shovel

___ 2. electrical   b. spray   ___ 7. gas   g. cord

___ 3. bug   c. gloves   ___ 8. snow   h. hose

___ 4. step   d. tape   ___ 9. extension   i. clippers

___ 5. work   e. measure   ___ 10. hedge   j. can

D. LISTENING: WHAT ARE THEY TALKING ABOUT?

Listen to the conversation. Circle the correct word.

1. hose	(gloves)	4. glue	fuse	7. fertilizer	nozzle
2. shovel	trowel	5. fly swatter	step ladder	8. mousetrap	insect spray
3. tape measure	plunger	6. hoe	oil	9. lawnmower	wheelbarrow

A. MATCHING: *CARDINAL AND ORDINAL NUMBERS*

_c_ **1.** four
___ **2.** one
___ **3.** three
___ **4.** two
___ **5.** five
___ **6.** twelve
___ **7.** eight
___ **8.** fourteen

a. fifth
b. twelfth
c. fourth
d. third
e. fourteenth
f. second
g. first
h. eighth

B. WHICH NUMBER?

1. There are ((fifteen) fifteenth) students in the class.

2. We live on the (nine   ninth) floor of an apartment building.

3. This is the (three   third) time I've been in this country.

4. My daughter is (ten   tenth) years old.

5. Today is our (twenty   twentieth) wedding anniversary.

6. This is my (twenty-one   twenty-first) birthday!

7. We'll have (fifty   fiftieth) people at the party.

8. This is the (one   first) time I've seen this movie.

C. CROSSWORD: *NUMBERS TO WORDS*

ACROSS

1. 17
3. 10
4. 20
5. 14th
7. 9th
8. 70

DOWN

1. 6
2. 8
3. 12
4. 3rd
5. 40th
6. 90
9. 2

¹S E V ²E N T E E N

D. LISTENING: *WHAT'S THE NUMBER?*

Circle the correct number.

1. (nine)   five
2. fifth   first
3. 14   40
4. 7th   11th
5. 20   11
6. 32   42
7. 55   65
8. 13th   30th

A. MATCHING: *WORDS*

_c_ **1.** plus   **a.** multiplication

___ **2.** times   **b.** division

___ **3.** minus   **c.** addition

___ **4.** divided by   **d.** subtraction

B. MATCHING: *NUMBERS AND WORDS*

_d_ **1.** 8 divided by 4 equals 2.   **a.** addition

___ **2.** 4 times 3 equals 12.   **b.** subtraction

___ **3.** 6 plus 2 equals 8.   **c.** multiplication

___ **4.** 9 minus 6 equals 3.   **d.** division

___ **5.** 8 times 2 equals 16.   **e.** $16 - 8 = 8$

___ **6.** 16 divided by 8 is 2.   **f.** $8 \times 2 = 16$

___ **7.** 16 minus 8 equals 8.   **g.** $8 + 8 = 16$

___ **8.** 8 plus 8 is 16.   **h.** $16 \div 8 = 2$

C. MATH SENTENCES

Write the math problems for these sentences.

$3 \times 6 = 18$			

1. *Three times six is eighteen.*   **2.** *Twenty minus six equals fourteen.*   **3.** *Six plus twelve is eighteen.*   **4.** *Twenty divided by two equals ten.*

D. MATCHING: *WORDS AND FRACTIONS*

_c_ **1.** three fourths   **a.** 1/4

___ **2.** two thirds   **b.** 1/2

___ **3.** one quarter   **c.** 3/4

___ **4.** one half   **d.** 1/3

___ **5.** one third   **e.** 2/3

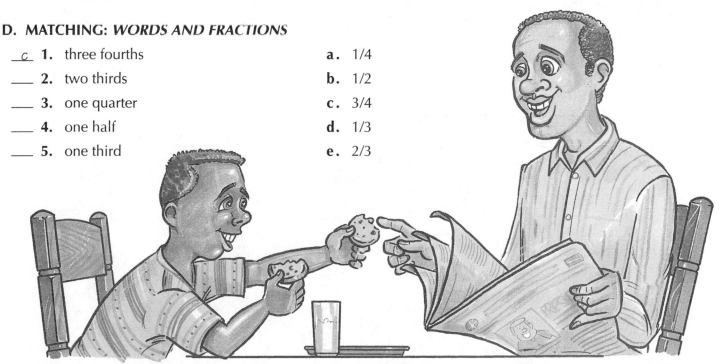

E. WHAT FRACTION IS IT?

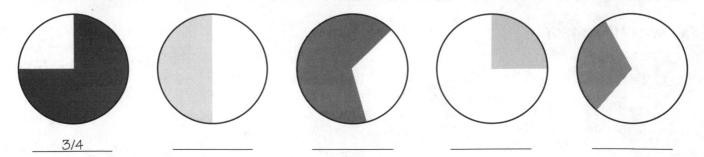

3/4   _____   _____   _____   _____

F. LISTENING: *WHAT'S THE FRACTION?*

Listen and write the number under the correct fraction.

1/2	3/4	2/3	1/3	1/4
_____	_____	_____	1 _____	_____

G. MATCHING: *WORDS AND PERCENTS*

_c_ **1.** fifty percent   **a.** 100%

___ **2.** seventy-five percent   **b.** 25%

___ **3.** one hundred percent   **c.** 50%

___ **4.** twenty-five percent   **d.** 60%

___ **5.** fifteen percent   **e.** 75%

___ **6.** sixty percent   **f.** 15%

H. WHAT PERCENT IS IT?

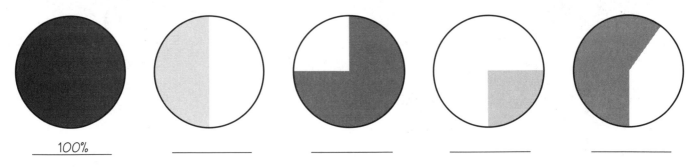

100%   _____   _____   _____   _____

I. LISTENING: *WHAT'S THE PERCENT?*

Listen and write the number under the correct percent.

25%	75%	50%	100%	60%
_____	_____	_____	1 _____	_____

J. CLASS PERCENTAGE

1. What percent of your class has brown hair?   . . . .

2. What percent of your class has blue eyes?   . . . .

3. What percent of your class speaks more than two languages?   . . . .

4. What percent of your class speaks more than three languages?   . . . .

A. WHAT TIME IS IT?

1. _____4:30_____

2. _____

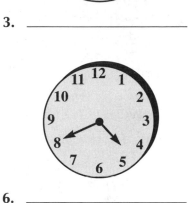

3. _____

4. _____

5. _____

6. _____

B. MATCHING: *TIME*

Draw a line to the correct time. Then draw a line to the correct words.

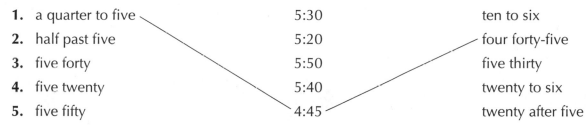

1. a quarter to five		5:30		ten to six
2. half past five		5:20		four forty-five
3. five forty		5:50		five thirty
4. five twenty		5:40		twenty to six
5. five fifty		4:45		twenty after five

C. WHEN IS IT?

midnight	noon	P.M.	A.M.

1. I usually have breakfast at 7:00 _____.

2. We often eat lunch at _____.

3. Happy New Year! It's exactly _____!

4. Dinner will be served at 7:00 _____.

D. LISTENING: *WHAT'S THE TIME?*

Listen and circle the correct time.

1. (3:00)   3:30   **3.** 1:05   5:01   **5.** 3:45   4:15

2. 10:05   5:10   **4.** 7:05   5:07   **6.** 8:15   7:45

E. THE TIMES OF YOUR LIFE

What time do you usually . . . .

1. ...get up?   . . . .   **3.** ...go to school or work?   . . . .   **5.** ...eat dinner?   . . . .

2. ...eat breakfast?   . . . .   **4.** ...have lunch?   . . . .   **6.** ...go to sleep?   . . . .

A. TODAY

1. What year is it? .... 3. What day is it? ....
2. What month is it? .... 4. What's today's date? ....

B. USING THE CALENDAR

Look at the calendar on page 33 of the Picture Dictionary. Write your answers.

What day of the week is . . .

1. January 14? _____Thursday_____ 4. January 5? _____
2. January 22? _____ 5. January 11? _____
3. January 2? _____ 6. January 20? _____

C. DATES: *WORDS TO NUMBERS*

Write the date using numbers.

1. September 3, 1949 = _9_ / _3_ / _49_ 4. February 12, 1995 = ___/___/___
2. January 16, 1970 = ___/___/___ 5. November 10, 1976 = ___/___/___
3. March 26, 1983 = ___/___/___ 6. December 12, 1912 = ___/___/___

D. DATES: *NUMBERS TO WORDS*

Write the date using words.

1. 4/16/78 = _____April 16, 1978_____ 4. 7/20/95 = _____
2. 10/1/96 = _____ 5. 5/25/56 = _____
3. 8/26/80 = _____ 6. 9/3/85 = _____

E. SEQUENCE

Put the months in the correct order.

_____ March   _____ June   _____ November   _____ May
_____ April   _____ February   _____ October   _1_ January
_____ December   _____ July   _____ August   _____ September

F. JOURNAL ENTRY

What are the names and dates of special holidays and celebrations in your country?

....
....
....
....
....
....
....

A. MAKING A LIST

Look at pages 34-35 in the Picture Dictionary and list 7 places to buy food.

_____ bakery _____   _____

_____   _____

_____   _____

_____

B. WHICH PLACE?

1. I'm getting a haircut today at the ((barber shop)   clinic).

2. I'm going to buy bread at the (bank   bakery).

3. Please pick up my coat and my suit at the (dry cleaners   service station).

4. I'll get some medicine at the (health club   pharmacy).

5. Look! There's a sale on sofas and tables at this (furniture store   appliance store)!

6. You can pick up a sandwich and soda at the (concert hall   delicatessen).

7. I'm going to the (service station   convenience store) to get gas and check the oil.

8. Let's get breakfast at the (discount store   donut shop).

9. We bought a beautiful bouquet of roses at the new (computer store   flower shop).

10. We enjoyed the music at the (hospital   concert hall) last night.

C. CROSSWORD: *PICTURES TO WORDS*

ACROSS

DOWN

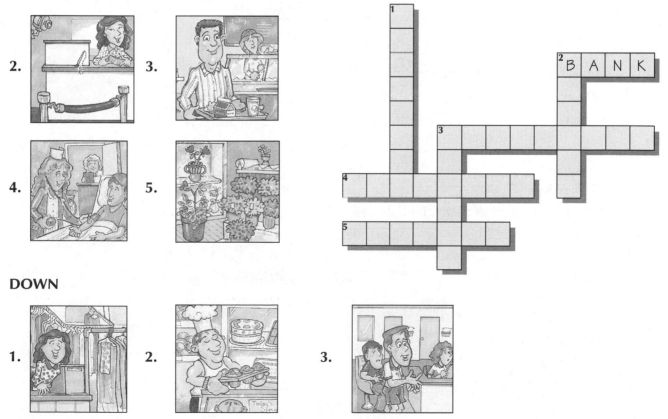

A. GOING SHOPPING

We like to shop at the _m_ _a_ _l_ _l_ [1]. We always park in the _ _ _ _ _ _ [2]. We buy cassette tapes and CDs at the _ _ _ _ _ [3] store. We look at the puppies and kittens at the _ _ _ [4] shop. We buy film for our camera at the _ _ _ _ _ [5] shop. Our children like to go to the _ _ _ [6] store to see all the things to play with. When we get hungry, we eat at the _ _ _ _ _ [7] shop or go to a _ _ _ _ _ _ _ _ _ _ [8]. We sometimes go to a movie at the movie _ _ _ _ _ _ _ [9]. We spend a lot of time at the mall!

B. ANALOGIES

| travel agency | music store | library | post office | jewelry store | vision centre |

1. food : supermarket *as* eyeglasses : _____vision centre_____
2. toys : toy store *as* jewelry : _____
3. pet shop : zoo *as* book store : _____
4. film : photo shop *as* stamps : _____
5. mothers : maternity shop *as* travelers : _____
6. shoes : shoe store *as* CDs : _____

C. MATCHING: *PLACES AND ACTIONS*

_c_ **1.** night club
___ **2.** zoo
___ **3.** museum
___ **4.** mall
___ **5.** motel
___ **6.** supermarket
___ **7.** library
___ **8.** laundromat

a. sleep away from home
b. shop at many stores
c. listen to music
d. borrow books
e. wash clothes
f. see special things from the past
g. buy groceries
h. learn about animals

D. LISTENING: *WHERE ARE THEY?*

Listen to the conversation and circle the correct place.

1. (movie theatre)   video store
2. train station   motel
3. pet shop   jewelry store
4. travel agency   school
5. shoe store   toy store
6. library   restaurant
7. pizza shop   museum
8. parking garage   ice cream shop

A. WHERE IS IT?

Look at pages 38-39 of the Picture Dictionary and write the answers.

1. There is a taxi in front of the b u s .

2. The subway is under the _ _ _ _ _ _ .

3. The garbage container is on the _ _ _ _ _ _ _ _ .

4. The ice cream truck is on the corner, in front of the _ _ _ _ _ _ _ _ .

5. The police station is next to the _ _ _ _ _ _ _ _ _ _ _ .

6. The courthouse is across from the _ _ _ _ _ _ _ _ _ _ _ _ .

7. The newsstand is across from the _ _ _ _ _ _ _ _ _ _ _ .

8. The police officer is in the _ _ _ _ _ _ _ _ _ _ _ _ _ _ .

B. MATCHING: *ASSOCIATIONS*

_d_	**1.** taxi	**a.**	garbage truck
___	**2.** newspapers	**b.**	crosswalk
___	**3.** pedestrian	**c.**	newsstand
___	**4.** fire alarm box	**d.**	taxi stand
___	**5.** police station	**e.**	fire station
___	**6.** garbage container	**f.**	jail

C. IN THE CITY

parking enforcement officer	newsstand	restaurant	intersection
taxi	crosswalk	street sign	public telephone

1. Pedestrians wait for the green light and then walk in the _____ crosswalk _____ .

2. The _____ tells the name of the street.

3. It costs twenty-five cents to use a _____ .

4. You can buy newspapers at the _____ .

5. Use the drive-through window when you go to the _____ .

6. Wait at the taxi stand to get a _____ .

7. A police officer directs traffic at the _____ of Main Street and Central Avenue.

8. When you don't put enough money in a parking meter, a _____ gives you a ticket.

D. JOURNAL ENTRY

Draw a sketch of an intersection near your home and describe it.

A. WHAT'S THE ANSWER?

Write the correct answer.

1. Is his hair short?

No. It's _____long_____ .

2. Are they good?

No. They're _____ .

3. Is she short?

No. She's _____ .

4. Are his pants tight?

No. They're _____ .

5. Is the water cold?

No. It's _____ .

6. Is she married?

No. She's _____ .

7. Is the street narrow?

No. It's _____ .

8. Are the clothes dry?

No. They're _____ .

9. Are the dishes clean?

No. They're _____ .

B. ANTONYMS

Write the correct opposite.

1. an old man – a _____young_____ man

2. an old car – a _____ car

3. a light package – a _____ package

4. a light room – a _____ room

5. a dull pencil – a _____ pencil

6. a dull floor – a _____ floor

7. a short woman – a _____ woman

8. a short dress – a _____ dress

9. a hard test – an _____ test

10. a hard pillow – a _____ pillow

11. straight hair – _____ hair

12. a straight road – a _____ road

C. MY CAR

I bought a car yesterday. It isn't (empty (new))[1].
As a matter of fact, it's very (soft old)[2], but it's clean
and (messy neat)[3]. It's not (fast curly)[4], but it's very
(quiet crooked)[5]. It's not a (fancy thick)[6] car, but
it's (pretty ugly)[7]. It's very economical. It's (small narrow)[8],
and it won't need a lot of gas. Best of all, the price was (good high)[9].
It was very (inexpensive wealthy)[10] and I like it a lot!

D. CROSSWORD: *OPPOSITES*

Complete the crossword using the *opposites* of the word clues.

ACROSS

4. expensive
6. dry
8. hard
10. crooked
11. cold
12. fancy
13. dull
15. smooth
16. wealthy

DOWN

1. loud
2. slow
3. ugly
5. difficult
7. ugly
9. thick
14. wide

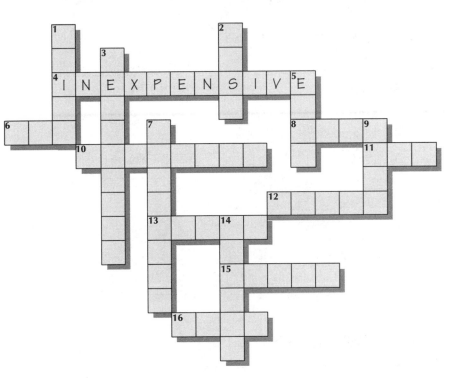

E. JOURNAL ENTRY

Write a word that describes . . . .

1. your street: . . . .
2. your neighbours: . . . .
3. your best friend: . . . .
4. your family: . . . .
5. your hair: . . . .
6. your classroom: . . . .

A. WHICH COLUMN?

happy emotions:

_____ proud _____

_____

_____

sad emotions:

_____

_____

_____

proud
annoyed
ecstatic
miserable
disappointed
pleased
frustrated

B. WHICH WORD?

1. I need a sweater. It's ((cold) hot) out!
2. I'm (surprised   disgusted)! I got an *A* on my test!
3. I'm (confused   thirsty). Let's get something to drink.
4. He feels (sick   full). I'm going to take him to the doctor.
5. You look (pretty   exhausted). Go to bed early tonight.

C. MATCHING: *ASSOCIATIONS*

_e_ 1. ill
___ 2. thirsty
___ 3. confused
___ 4. hungry
___ 5. tired

a. sleep
b. information
c. food
d. drink
e. medicine

D. ANALOGIES

unhappy	ecstatic	cold	sick	tired

1. mad : furious *as* happy : _____ ecstatic _____
2. scared : afraid *as* ill : _____
3. proud : ashamed *as* hot : _____
4. miserable : sad *as* exhausted : _____
5. angry : mad *as* sad : _____

E. JOURNAL ENTRY

Finish the sentences.

1. When someone interrupts me, I feel . . . .
2. When someone cuts in front of me in line, I feel . . . .
3. When someone bangs into the back of my car, I feel . . . .
4. When a big boy hits a little boy, I feel . . . .
5. When I see . . . ., I feel . . . .
6. When . . . ., I feel . . . .

A. WHICH FRUIT DOESN'T BELONG?

Which fruit . . .

1. isn't a berry?	strawberry	lime	blueberry	raspberry
2. isn't a citrus fruit?	coconut	grapefruit	tangerine	lemon
3. isn't a melon?	watermelon	apricot	honeydew	cantaloupe
4. doesn't have a pit?	peach	pineapple	plum	avocado
5. doesn't grow on a tree?	apple	orange	nectarine	strawberry

B. LISTENING: *WHAT FRUIT ARE THEY TALKING ABOUT?*

1. apples	apricots	**5.** watermelon	lemon
2. plums	prunes	**6.** tangerines	nectarines
3. banana	papaya	**7.** cherries	cranberries
4. grapes	dates	**8.** coconut	apricot

C. CROSSWORD: *PICTURES TO WORDS*

ACROSS

3.    **5.**

6.    **8.**

9.

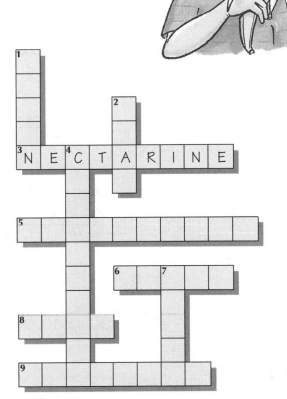

DOWN

1.   **2.**

4. 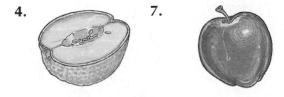   **7.**

A. WHICH GROUP?

zucchini	lima bean	yam	scallion

1. string bean   black bean   _lima bean_
2. acorn squash   butternut squash
3. potato   sweet potato
4. red onion   pearl onion

B. MATCHING

_b_ 1. sweet   **a.** sprouts
___ 2. red   **b.** potato
___ 3. brussels   **c.** squash
___ 4. acorn   **d.** bean
___ 5. string   **e.** pepper

C. CROSSWORD: *PICTURES TO WORDS*

ACROSS

2.   5.

6.   8.

9.

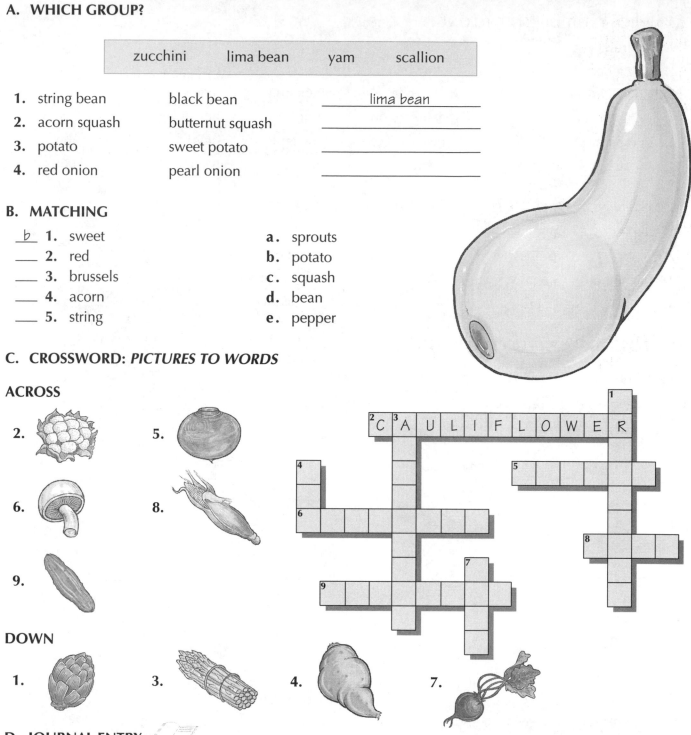

DOWN

1.   3.   4.   7.

D. JOURNAL ENTRY

People in different countries eat vegetables in different ways. In your country, which vegetables do people eat raw (uncooked)? Which vegetables do people cook before they eat?

Raw: Cooked:

....
....
....
....

A. WHICH GROUP?

canned vegetables	cereal	cheese	eggs
diet pop	milk	noodles	bottled water
rice	pop	soup	tuna fish

Packaged Goods: _____

Beverages: _____

Canned Goods: _____
    canned vegetables

Dairy Products: _____

B. WHICH WORD?

1. I need skim ((milk)   punch) for my cereal.
2. We need sour (rice   cream).
3. We also need cottage (fruit   cheese).
4. Tuna (fish   noodle) is good for you.
5. How do you like the pineapple (juice   water)?
6. Finish your fruit (pack   juice).
7. Do we have any juice (fruit   packs)?
8. I'll get some diet (pop   cream).

C. MORE GROUPS

beef	bread	cake	chicken	duck	rolls
salmon	roast	flounder	lamb	shellfish	turkey

Meat:
    beef

Poultry:

Seafood:

Baked Goods:

D. WHERE ARE THEY?

Poultry	Meat	Seafood	Baked Goods	Frozen Foods

1. Drumsticks are in the _____Poultry_____ Section.
2. You can find sausages in the _____ Section.
3. Haddock is in the _____ Section.
4. You'll find rolls in the _____ Section.
5. Ice cream is in the _____ Section.

E. MATCHING: *WHERE ARE THESE FOODS?*

_e_ **1.** soup
___ **2.** pork
___ **3.** frozen lemonade
___ **4.** chicken
___ **5.** pop

a. Poultry
b. Meat
c. Beverages
d. Frozen Foods
e. Canned Goods

___ **6.** cereal
___ **7.** bread
___ **8.** eggs
___ **9.** grape juice
___ **10.** flounder

f. Dairy Products
g. Seafood
h. Packaged Goods
i. Baked Goods
j. Juice

F. WHAT'S THE WORD?

| rolls | lemonade | mussels | steak | trout | wings |

1. What chicken parts should I get—legs or _____wings_____?
2. What fish do you prefer—salmon or _____?
3. What should I get to drink—orange juice or _____?
4. Would you like shellfish? We have oysters or _____.
5. Beef is on sale today. How about a roast, or a _____?
6. Should we make the sandwiches with pita bread or _____?

G. LISTENING: *WHAT ARE THEY TALKING ABOUT?*

Circle the correct word.

1. cake   (steak)
2. duck   pork
3. ham   lamb
4. shrimp   ribs

5. halibut   haddock
6. roast   trout
7. oysters   lobsters
8. eggs   legs

H. JOURNAL ENTRY

Describe how people shop for food in your country.

....
....
....
....
....

A. WHICH GROUP?

mozzarella	cocoa	bologna	relish	pretzels	cole slaw

1. Swiss cheese   provolone   _mozzarella_
2. nuts   popcorn   _____
3. potato salad   macaroni salad   _____
4. coffee   tea   _____
5. corned beef   roast beef   _____
6. ketchup   mustard   _____

B. MATCHING

_c_ 1. olive   **a.** sauce
___ 2. herbal   **b.** beef
___ 3. corn   **c.** oil
___ 4. cole   **d.** chips
___ 5. corned   **e.** tea
___ 6. soy   **f.** slaw

C. MATCHING: *ASSOCIATIONS*

_c_ 1. straws   **a.** weigh
___ 2. soap   **b.** read
___ 3. tabloid   **c.** drink
___ 4. cashier   **d.** clean
___ 5. scale   **e.** chew
___ 6. gum   **f.** pay

D. WHICH WORD?

1. I only need a few things. I'll get a shopping (cart   basket).
2. Use paper (towels   bags) to clean up the mess.
3. I forgot to get disposable (diapers   wrap).
4. Household items are in the next (aisle   counter).
5. Do you want a paper or plastic (wrap   bag)?
6. Shoppers can save money when they use (coupons   the cash register).

E. LISTENING: *WHAT SECTION?*

Listen to the conversation and circle the correct section.

1. (Paper Products)   Baking Products
2. Household Items   Checkout Area
3. Baby Products   Dairy Products
4. Coffee and Tea   Snack Foods
5. Baking Products   Jams and Jellies
6. Meat Section   Deli
7. Deli   Condiments
8. Snack Foods   Paper Products

CONTAINERS AND QUANTITIES

A. WHAT'S THE CONTAINER?

bunch	bag	roll	can	box	jar

box
- cereal
- crackers
- raisins

_____
- toilet paper
- paper towels
- wax paper

_____
- potato chips
- flour
- pretzels

_____
- bananas
- grapes
- carrots

_____
- soup
- tuna fish
- soda

_____
- baby food
- mayonnaise
- jelly

B. WHAT'S THE WORD?

dozen	loaf	ear	box	head	bar	kilogram	litre

1. a _____kilogram_____ of meat
2. a _____ of lettuce
3. a _____ of soap
4. a _____ of milk
5. a _____ of bread
6. a _____ eggs
7. a _____ of crackers
8. an _____ of corn

C. WHICH WORD?

1. I got a ((tub) carton) of margarine.
2. I have two (loaves packs) of gum.
3. Please get a (roll stick) of aluminum foil.
4. Can you get a (litre bunch) of ice cream?
5. We need a (six-pack stick) of butter.
6. Don't forget to buy a (head pack) of lettuce.

D. LISTENING: WHAT ARE THEY TALKING ABOUT?

Listen to the conversation and circle the correct words.

1. a six-pack   (two six-packs)
2. a loaf   two loaves
3. a litre   two litres
4. pack   package
5. bottle   carton
6. a few ears   two ears
7. kilogram   litre
8. boxes   bunches

UNITS OF MEASURE

A. MATCHING: *ABBREVIATIONS*

<u>d</u> **1.** teaspoon   **a.** Tbsp.

___ **2.** tablespoon   **b.** k

___ **3.** millilitre   **c.** g

___ **4.** litre   **d.** tsp.

___ **5.** gram   **e.** L

___ **6.** kilogram   **f.** mL

B. WHICH IS EQUAL?

<u>c</u> **1.** 5 mL   **a.** 1 tablespoon

___ **2.** 250 mL   **b.** half a litre

___ **3.** 15 mL   **c.** 1 cup

___ **4.** 500 mL   **d.** 1 teaspoon

C. WHICH WORD?

1. The recipe says to add 8 ((tablespoons) litres) of butter.

2. I need (250 g   250 mL) of ground beef, please.

3. There are two (kilograms   cups) of orange juice in this punch.

4. Add a (teaspoon   kilogram) of salt to the chili.

5. I bought a (kilogram   litre) of milk at the supermarket yesterday.

6. The recipe says to put half a (kilogram   cup) of cream into the mixture.

D. WHAT'S THE NUMBER?

1. 250 mL   =   <u> 1 </u> cup   **4.** 1 L   =   _____ cups

2. 500 mL   =   _____ cups   **5.** 30 mL   =   _____ Tbsp.

3. 1000 mL   =   _____ litre   **6.** 6 tsps.   =   _____ Tbsp.

E. LISTENING

Listen and circle the correct words.

1. two kilograms   (two cups)   **5.** two teaspoons   two tablespoons

2. a cup   a quarter   **6.** 250 grams   200 grams

3. a tablespoon   a teaspoon   **7.** half a gram   100 grams

4. a kilogram   half a kilogram   **8.** carton   litre

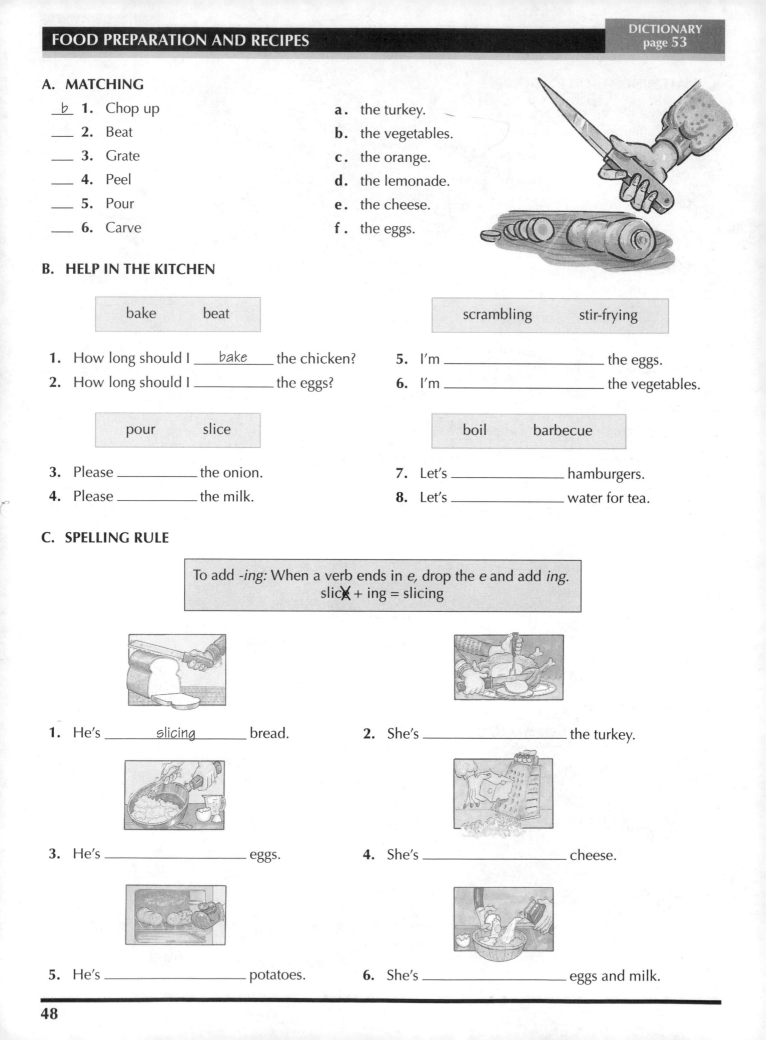

A. MATCHING

_b_ **1.** Chop up

___ **2.** Beat

___ **3.** Grate

___ **4.** Peel

___ **5.** Pour

___ **6.** Carve

a. the turkey.

b. the vegetables.

c. the orange.

d. the lemonade.

e. the cheese.

f. the eggs.

B. HELP IN THE KITCHEN

bake	beat

1. How long should I ___bake___ the chicken?

2. How long should I _____ the eggs?

scrambling	stir-frying

5. I'm _____ the eggs.

6. I'm _____ the vegetables.

pour	slice

3. Please _____ the onion.

4. Please _____ the milk.

boil	barbecue

7. Let's _____ hamburgers.

8. Let's _____ water for tea.

C. SPELLING RULE

To add -*ing:* When a verb ends in *e,* drop the *e* and add *ing.*
slic~~e~~ + ing = slicing

1. He's ___slicing___ bread.

2. She's _____ the turkey.

3. He's _____ eggs.

4. She's _____ cheese.

5. He's _____ potatoes.

6. She's _____ eggs and milk.

FAST FOODS AND SANDWICHES

A. ORDERING FAST FOOD

_c_ **1.** I'd like a slice of   **a.** coffee.

___ **2.** I'll have a bowl of   **b.** sandwich.

___ **3.** I'll have an order of   **c.** pizza.

___ **4.** I'd like a bacon, lettuce, and tomato   **d.** chili.

___ **5.** I'll have a small decaf   **e.** fried chicken.

B. WHICH WORD DOESN'T BELONG?

1. tea	lemonade	milk	(taco)
2. roll	bun	BLT	bagel
3. tuna fish	roast beef	iced tea	hamburger
4. donut	pumpernickel	whole wheat	rye
5. roast beef	hamburger	corned beef	chicken
6. danish	pita bread	submarine roll	white bread

C. LISTENING: *TAKING FAST FOOD ORDERS*

Listen to the order and put a check next to the correct item.

1. ✓ roast beef   **4.** ___ danish

___ corned beef   ___ tuna fish

2. ___ tuna fish   **5.** ___ chili

___ biscuit   ___ BLT

3. ___ taco   **6.** ___ rye bread

___ hot dog   ___ white bread

D. JOURNAL ENTRY

Are any of the fast foods or sandwiches on page 54 of the Picture Dictionary popular in your country?
Which ones? What other foods are popular for a quick meal or snack?

....

....

....

....

....

....

....

....

A. ORDERING

Fill in the blanks, and then practise the conversation with a friend.

| apple pie | veal cutlet | noodles | shrimp cocktail | antipasto |

May I take your order?
   Yes, please. For an appetizer, I'd like the _____shrimp cocktail_____[1].
And what kind of salad would you like?
   I'd like the _____[2].
And for the main course?
   I think I'll have the _____[3], please.
What side dish would you like with that?
   I'll have the _____[4].
Would you care for dessert?
   Yes. I'll have _____[5], please.

B. LISTENING: ORDERING AT A RESTAURANT

You're a waiter or waitress! Listen to the order and check the correct items.

1.

Appetizers
___ fruit cup/fruit cocktail	___ nachos
___ tomato juice	___ chicken wings
___ shrimp cocktail	✓ potato skins

Salads
___ tossed salad	___ antipasto
___ Greek salad	___ Caesar salad
___ spinach salad	___ salad bar

Main Courses/Entrees
___ meatloaf	___ baked chicken
___ roast beef	___ broiled fish
___ veal cutlet	___ spaghetti

Side Dishes
___ baked potato	___ rice
___ mashed potatoes	___ noodles
___ french fries	___ mixed vegetables

Desserts
___ chocolate cake	___ jello
___ apple pie	___ pudding
___ ice cream	___ an ice cream sundae

2.

Appetizers
___ fruit cup/fruit cocktail	___ nachos
___ tomato juice	___ chicken wings
___ shrimp cocktail	___ potato skins

Salads
___ tossed salad	___ antipasto
___ Greek salad	___ Caesar salad
___ spinach salad	___ salad bar

Main Courses/Entrees
___ meatloaf	___ baked chicken
___ roast beef	___ broiled fish
___ veal cutlet	___ spaghetti

Side Dishes
___ baked potato	___ rice
___ mashed potatoes	___ noodles
___ french fries	___ mixed vegetables

Desserts
___ chocolate cake	___ jello
___ apple pie	___ pudding
___ ice cream	___ an ice cream sundae

C. ROLE PLAY

You are now the owner of a popular restaurant in your country! Create a menu for your restaurant.

_____'s Restaurant
(Your Name)

Appetizers

_____   _____
_____   _____
_____   _____
_____   _____

Salads

_____   _____
_____   _____
_____   _____
_____   _____

Main Courses / Entrees

_____   _____
_____   _____
_____   _____
_____   _____

Side Dishes

_____   _____
_____   _____
_____   _____
_____   _____

Desserts

_____   _____
_____   _____
_____   _____
_____   _____

Beverages

_____   _____
_____   _____
_____   _____

Now give the menu to some friends who are your restaurant customers, and take down their order.

A. MATCHING: ASSOCIATIONS

_c_ **1.** strawberries

___ **2.** a lemon

___ **3.** a carrot

___ **4.** blueberries

___ **5.** lettuce

___ **6.** eggplant

a. yellow

b. purple

c. red

d. green

e. orange

f. blue

B. WHICH COLOUR?

white	black	gold	red	blue	grey	green

1. Look at those ____grey____ clouds. I think a storm is coming.

2. What a beautiful _____ sky!

3. The grass is so _____!

4. The flag of Canada is _____ and _____.

5. _____ jewelry costs a lot of money.

6. We have an old _____ and _____ TV.

C. QUESTIONNAIRE

Fill in the information about yourself.

1. Colour of hair: . . . .

2. Colour of eyes: . . . .

3. Favourite colour: . . . .

4. Colours on your country's flag: . . . .

D. JOURNAL ENTRY

In Canada, baby girls often wear pink clothing. Baby boys often wear blue. At funerals, people usually wear black or dark clothing. In your country, what colours do people wear in different situations?

. . . .

. . . .

. . . .

. . . .

. . . .

. . . .

. . . .

. . . .

. . . .

A. WHICH WORD?

| sweater | gown | skirt | shirt | suit | jacket |

1. I really like your new short-sleeved _____ shirt _____.
2. What a shame! She just ripped her evening _____.
3. I think I'll wear my new cardigan _____ tonight.
4. Where did you get your new sports _____?
5. Wear your three-piece _____ to the wedding.
6. It's too hot for pants. I think I'll wear my new _____.

B. MATCHING: COMPOUND WORDS

Draw a line to complete the word. Then write the word on the line.

1. jump   tie   _____ jumpsuit _____
2. turtle   neck   _____
3. over   suit   _____
4. neck   alls   _____

C. MAKING CLOTHES

Change the first letter to write a piece of clothing.

1. pie   t i e   5. best   _ _ _ _
2. press   _ _ _ _ _   6. down   _ _ _ _
3. beans   _ _ _ _ _   7. nights   _ _ _ _ _ _
4. boat   _ _ _ _   8. racket   _ _ _ _ _ _

D. CROSSWORD: PICTURES TO WORDS

ACROSS

1.   4.   5.

6.   7.   8.

DOWN

2.   3.   5.

6.   7.

A. WHICH WORD?

1. It's time for bed. Put on your ((pyjamas) work boots).

2. Take off your (long johns   work boots) before you come in the house.

3. I want to play tennis, but I can't find my (flip-flops   sneakers).

4. Those (hiking boots   slippers) look very nice with your nightgown.

5. It's very hot today! I think I'll wear my (high heels   sandals).

6. It's snowing outside! Wear your (boxer shorts   long underwear) when you go out.

7. You can wear this (robe   panty hose) over your nightgown.

B. WHICH WORD DOESN'T BELONG?

1. pumps	(underpants)	loafers	sneakers
2. stockings	sandals	slippers	flip-flops
3. panties	boxer shorts	boots	underpants
4. socks	pyjamas	tights	stockings
5. boots	slip	shoes	moccasins
6. panties	briefs	socks	camisole

C. MATCHING

We wear these. . . .

_g_ **1.** . . . at the beach.

___ **2.** . . . at a ball game.

___ **3.** . . . with a bathrobe.

___ **4.** . . . climbing a mountain.

___ **5.** . . . with a fancy dress.

___ **6.** . . . jogging through a park.

___ **7.** . . . at a construction site.

a. running shoes

b. sneakers

c. high heels

d. slippers

e. work boots

f. hiking boots

g. flip-flops

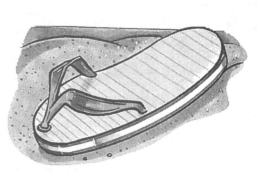

D. LISTENING: *WHAT ARE THEY TALKING ABOUT?*

Listen to the conversation and circle the correct word.

1. athletic supporter   (shorts)

2. high tops   flip-flops

3. slippers   slip

4. pumps   briefs

5. pyjamas   panties

6. stockings   socks

7. nightshirt   undershirt

8. shorts   shoes

A. WHICH GROUP?

windbreaker	beret	running shorts	parka	down vest
cap	tennis shorts	rain hat	sweat pants	

jackets	hats	pants
windbreaker	_____	_____
_____	_____	_____
_____	_____	_____

B. WHAT DO WE WEAR?

rubbers	shorts	ski jacket	poncho	mittens
tank top	ear muffs	raincoat	sandals	

. . . when it's hot?	. . . when it's raining?	. . . when it's snowing?
_____	_rubbers_	_____
_____	_____	_____
_____	_____	_____

C. MATCHING: WHICH PART OF THE BODY?

_e_ **1.** ear muffs   **a.** face and head

___ **2.** sweatband   **b.** feet

___ **3.** gloves   **c.** legs

___ **4.** scarf   **d.** forehead

___ **5.** rubbers   **e.** ears

___ **6.** tights   **f.** hands

___ **7.** ski mask   **g.** neck

D. LISTENING: WHAT ARE THEY TALKING ABOUT?

Listen to the conversation and circle the correct word.

1. (hat)   cap   **5.** beret   parka

2. poncho   overcoat   **6.** parka   scarf

3. sweatband   sweat pants   **7.** ski mask   ear muffs

4. lycra shorts   trenchcoat   **8.** mittens   tennis shorts

A. WHERE DO WE WEAR THEM?

| ring | necklace | bracelet | beads | belt | watch | wedding band | chain |

neck	finger	wrist	waist
_____	ring	_____	_____
_____	_____	_____	
_____			

B. MATCHING: *HOW DO WE USE THEM?*

_d_ **1.** We use these to connect the cuffs of fancy shirts.

___ **2.** We use this to connect a tie with the shirt.

___ **3.** We use this to keep pants up.

___ **4.** We keep credit cards and money in this.

___ **5.** We carry books in this.

___ **6.** We use this to keep keys together.

___ **7.** We use this to protect us from the rain.

___ **8.** We keep coins in this.

a. book bag

b. belt

c. change purse

d. cuff links

e. tie clip

f. umbrella

g. key chain

h. wallet

C. MATCHING: *COMPOUND WORDS*

Draw a line to complete the word. Then write the word on the line.

1. neck	ring	necklace
2. pocket	book	_____
3. hand	bag	_____
4. back	case	_____
5. brief	pack	_____
6. ear	lace	_____

D. WHICH WORD DOESN'T BELONG?

1. briefcase	book bag	backpack	(wallet)
2. necklace	key chain	pearls	beads
3. ring	wedding band	key ring	engagement ring
4. bracelet	purse	pocketbook	handbag
5. ring	earrings	bracelet	tote bag

A. WHAT'S THE WORD?

dark	baggy	wide	heavy	low	plain

1. How do you like this fancy tie?
   Actually, I prefer that _____plain_____ one.

2. Shoes with high heels look attractive.
   Yes, but shoes with _____ heels are much more comfortable.

3. These narrow shoes are tight!
   Why don't you try on _____ shoes?

4. Do you think these jeans are too tight?
   No. Actually, I think they're _____.

5. Is it cool enough for a light sweater?
   Actually, I think you should wear a _____ one.

6. Can I wear this light tie with this suit?
   No. A _____ tie looks better.

B. WHAT'S THE WORD?

1. This (low (striped)) shirt is half-price.
2. These shoes are too (narrow   baggy).
3. I prefer the (baggy   high) pants.
4. My coat is too (paisley   long).
5. The hiking boots look (light   dark), but they're heavy.
6. This cap is too (short   small) for his head.
7. He prefers to wear a (narrow   tight) tie.
8. The pants are too big and (long   short).

C. LISTENING: *WHAT ARE THEY DESCRIBING?*

Listen to the conversation. Put the number next to the correct description.

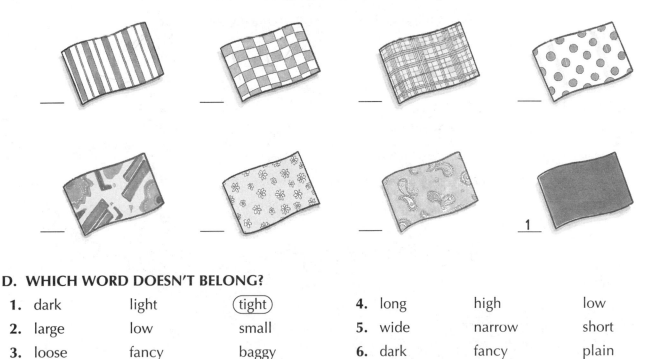

___   ___   ___   ___

___   ___   ___   1

D. WHICH WORD DOESN'T BELONG?

1.	dark	light	(tight)	4.	long	high	low
2.	large	low	small	5.	wide	narrow	short
3.	loose	fancy	baggy	6.	dark	fancy	plain

A. MATCHING: *DEPARTMENTS*

_e_ **1.** a tie

___ **2.** a necklace

___ **3.** a lamp

___ **4.** a dress

___ **5.** a refrigerator

___ **6.** an iron

___ **7.** pyjamas for a young boy

___ **8.** a television

a. Jewelry Counter

b. Furniture

c. Women's Clothing

d. Housewares

e. Men's Clothing

f. Electronics

g. Household Appliances

h. Children's Clothing

B. WHICH WORD?

1. I'm hungry. Let's go to the ((snack bar) Customer Assistance Counter).

2. Where's the Perfume Counter? Let's look at the (water fountain   directory).

3. The car is on the second floor of the (parking lot   elevator).

4. Let's pick up the refrigerator at the (Gift Wrap Counter   customer pickup area).

5. Let's take the (escalator   customer pickup area) up to the third floor.

6. I'm thirsty. Is there a (Customer Service Counter   water fountain) nearby?

C. LISTENING

Listen to the conversation. Write the number next to the correct place.

___ Perfume Counter	___ Jewelry Counter
_1_ Electronics Department	___ elevator
___ parking garage	___ snack bar
___ Children's Clothing Department	___ escalator
___ Furniture Department	

D. JOURNAL ENTRY

In your country, where do people buy furniture, clothing, household appliances, and electronic equipment? Do they shop in large department stores or in smaller stores? Describe these places and the items they sell.

. . . .

. . . .

. . . .

. . . .

. . . .

. . . .

. . . .

. . . .

A. ANOTHER WAY OF SAYING IT

Look at page 63 of the Picture Dictionary. Find another way of saying the same thing.

1. CD = _compact disc_   5. camcorder = _____
2. TV = _television_   6. stereo system = _____
3. VCR = _____   7. portable stereo system = _____
4. Walkman = _____   8. tape = _____

B. MATCHING: *ASSOCIATIONS*

_c_ 1. VCR   a. record
___ 2. CD player   b. tuner
___ 3. tape recorder   c. videotape
___ 4. radio   d. compact disc
___ 5. turntable   e. audio cassette

C. ANALOGIES

| audio cassette | headphones | videotape | Walkman | turntable | VCR |

1. CD : record *as* CD player : _turntable_
2. audio cassette : tape deck *as* videotape : _____
3. camcorder : video camera *as* personal cassette player : _____
4. boom box : portable stereo system *as* audio tape : _____
5. tape recorder : audio tape *as* camcorder : _____
6. sound system : speaker *as* Walkman : _____

D. MATCHING: *IDENTIFYING EQUIPMENT*

We use this. . .

_e_ 1. to listen to different stations for news or music.   a. CD player
___ 2. to change the channel on television.   b. remote control
___ 3. to listen to compact discs.   c. set of headphones
___ 4. to listen to cassettes by ourselves.   d. clock radio
___ 5. to wake up to music in the morning.   e. radio

A. MATCHING: *WHAT EQUIPMENT DO YOU NEED?*

We use this. . . .

_e_ 1. to take a photograph.
___ 2. to show slides.
___ 3. to add, subtract, multiply, and divide.
___ 4. to type.
___ 5. to show a movie.
___ 6. to record a telephone message.
___ 7. to store information.
___ 8. to store a camera.

a. a calculator
b. a diskette
c. a camera case
d. a slide projector
e. a camera
f. an answering machine
g. a typewriter
h. a movie screen

B. MATCHING

_e_ 1. fax
___ 2. zoom
___ 3. flash
___ 4. floppy
___ 5. camera
___ 6. disk
___ 7. slide
___ 8. portable

a. drive
b. attachment
c. projector
d. telephone
e. machine
f. lens
g. disk
h. case

C. LISTENING: *USING A CHECKLIST*

Listen to the conversation. Check the equipment included.

1.
☑ monitor
___ disk drive
___ keyboard
___ mouse
___ printer
___ modem
___ software

2.
___ monitor
___ disk drive
___ keyboard
___ mouse
___ printer
___ modem
___ software

3.
___ camera
___ zoom lens
___ camera case
___ flash attachment
___ tripod
___ film

A. TOYS

| bicycle | train set | video game system | pail and shovel | jigsaw puzzle | skateboard |

Toys we use inside:

_____

_____

_____

Toys we use outside:

_____ bicycle _____

_____

_____

B. MATCHING

_e_ **1.** hula   **a.** rope

___ **2.** jump   **b.** animal

___ **3.** stuffed   **c.** house

___ **4.** doll   **d.** ball

___ **5.** rubber   **e.** hoop

___ **6.** model   **f.** puzzle

___ **7.** swing   **g.** figure

___ **8.** jigsaw   **h.** set

___ **9.** modeling   **i.** kit

___ **10.** action   **j.** clay

C. WHAT'S THE WORD?

| colouring book | construction set | doll house | paint set |
| rubber ball | stuffed animal | tricycle | wading pool |

1. You can use your new crayons in your _____ colouring book _____.

2. Let's play catch! Throw me that _____.

3. Billy likes to ride his _____ very much.

4. My daughter makes beautiful pictures with her _____.

5. My children built a city with bridges and parks with their _____.

6. It's hot! Let's cool off in the _____.

7. We bought small tables, chairs, rugs, and beds for Patty's _____.

8. My little boy always sleeps with his _____.

D. JOURNAL ENTRY

Write about a special toy you had when you were very young. Why was it special?

. . . .

. . . .

. . . .

. . . .

. . . .

. . . .

. . . .

MONEY

A. CANADIAN COINS

| penny | nickel | dime | quarter | loonie | two-dollar coin |

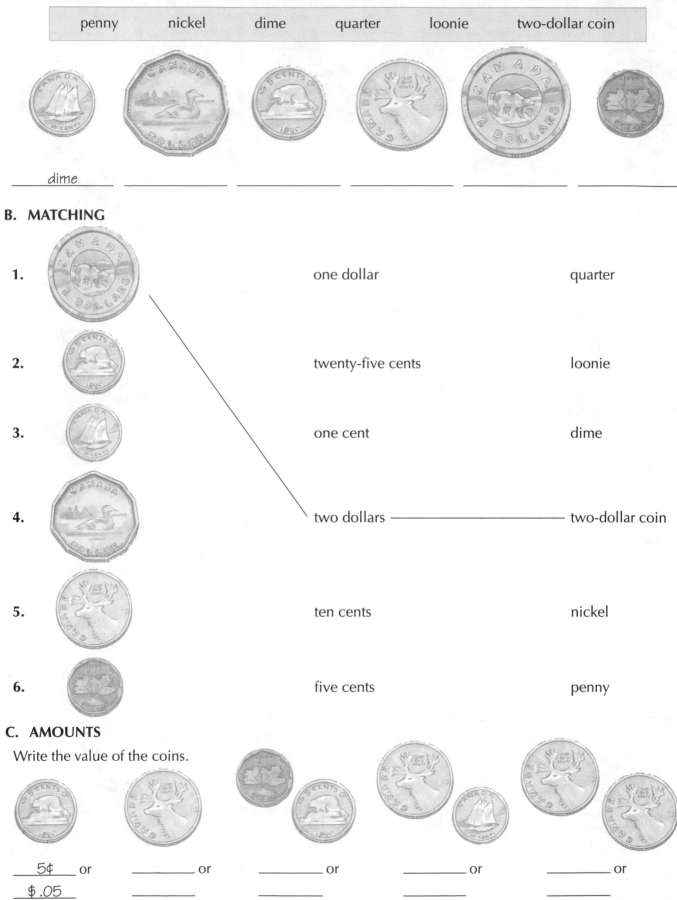

dime _____ _____ _____ _____ _____

B. MATCHING

1.

one dollar   quarter

2.

twenty-five cents   loonie

3.

one cent   dime

4.

two dollars ——————————— two-dollar coin

5.

ten cents   nickel

6.

five cents   penny

C. AMOUNTS

Write the value of the coins.

___5¢___ or   _____ or   _____ or   _____ or   _____ or
__$ .05__   _____   _____   _____   _____

D. CANADIAN CURRENCY

Write the value of the currency.

___$10.00___   _____   _____   _____   _____

E. MAKING CHANGE

1. That comes to $16.00.
   Okay. Here's $20.00.
   And your change is ___$ 4.00___.

2. That will be $.85.
   I have $1.00.
   And your change is _____.

3. And the total is $45.00.
   Here's $50.00.
   Your change is _____.

4. Your total is $8.00.
   I can give you _____.
   Fine. And your change is $2.00.

5. That's $.20.
   I have $.25.
   Okay. And your change is _____.

6. That comes to $99.00.
   Here's _____.
   And here's a dollar back.

F. LISTENING: *HOW MUCH?*

Listen to the conversation. Circle the correct amount.

1. ($10.00) $.10
2. $16.50 $6.50
3. $1.00 $.01
4. $55.00 $5.50

5. $5.10 $51.00
6. $23.50 $25.30
7. $14.50 $40.60
8. $12.10 $20.10

A. IN THE BANK

traveler's cheques	cheque	monthly statement	teller
chequebook	money order	deposit slip	withdrawal slip

1. Ask the _____ _teller_ _____ for change for $100.

2. We don't accept cash. You can write a _____ .

3. I need a _____ for $50.25, please.

4. I can't write a cheque. I don't have my _____ with me.

5. Don't carry a lot of cash when you go on vacation. It's a good idea to get _____ .

6. The bank will send your _____ in the mail.

7. To put the money in the bank, fill out this _____ .

8. To take money out of the bank, fill out a _____ .

B. MATCHING

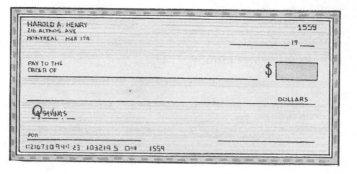

_d_ **1.** cheque	**a.** guard
___ **2.** credit	**b.** order
___ **3.** security	**c.** application
___ **4.** money	**d.** register
___ **5.** loan	**e.** card
___ **6.** monthly	**f.** cheques
___ **7.** automatic	**g.** statement
___ **8.** traveler's	**h.** teller

C. WHICH WORD DOESN'T BELONG?

1. teller	security guard	(automatic teller)	bank officer
2. safe deposit box	traveler's cheques	cheque	money order
3. deposit slip	loan application	ATM card	withdrawal slip
4. cheque register	security guard	monthly statement	bank book
5. cheque	chequebook	cheque register	loan application

HAROLD A. HENRY
216 ALTNOS AVE
MONTREAL H4R 1T4   1559

                                                        19 ___

PAY TO THE
ORDER OF _____ $ [   ]

_____ DOLLARS

SAVINGS _____

FOR _____

1:216730 94": 23 103219 5 0" 1559

D. WHAT ARE YOU DOING?

Follow the instructions.

WITHDRAWAL APPLICATION	Date _____
	CASH WITHDRAWAL	
2945 5879	CHEQUE WITHDRAWAL	
Account Number		
	TOTAL WITHDRAWAL	$150.00

Signature _____

WITHDRAWAL APPLICATION	Date _____
	CASH WITHDRAWAL	
Account Number	CHEQUE WITHDRAWAL	
	TOTAL WITHDRAWAL	

Signature _____

1. Withdraw $150.00.
    Your account number is 2945 5879.

2. Withdraw $250.00.
    Your account number is 1094 3875.

DEPOSIT SLIP	Date _____
	CURRENCY	
Account Number	COIN	
	CHEQUES	
Name		
Sign here ONLY if cash received from deposit	LESS CASH	
	TOTAL	

SAVINGS DEPOSIT SLIP	Date _____
	CURRENCY	
Account Number	COIN	
	CHEQUES	
Name		
Sign here ONLY if cash received from deposit	LESS CASH	
	TOTAL	

3. Deposit $650.50.
    Your account number is 595 40985.

4. Deposit $450.30.
    Your account number is 4378 349.

_____ 19 ___

Pay to the
order of _____ $ _____

_____ Dollars

Memo _____ _____

1:2110783

_____ 19 ___

Pay to the
order of _____ $ _____

_____ Dollars

Memo _____ _____

1:2110783

5. Write a cheque for $115.00 to a company or store.

6. Write a cheque for $36.85 to someone you know.

A. WHICH WORD DOESN'T BELONG?

1. knee   (earlobe)   calf   shin
2. iris   cornea   pupil   nose
3. tongue   beard   mustache   hair
4. forehead   nose   mouth   hip
5. calf   knee   shin   elbow
6. armpit   lip   teeth   tongue

B. MATCHING: *ASSOCIATIONS*

_c_	1. eyes	**a.** hear
___	2. ears	**b.** taste
___	3. nose	**c.** see
___	4. tongue	**d.** stand
___	5. teeth	**e.** smell
___	6. leg	**f.** chew

C. MATCHING: *CLOTHING AND THE BODY*

_e_	1. tie	**a.** ears
___	2. belt	**b.** waist
___	3. hat	**c.** lips
___	4. stockings	**d.** head
___	5. lipstick	**e.** neck
___	6. earrings	**f.** legs

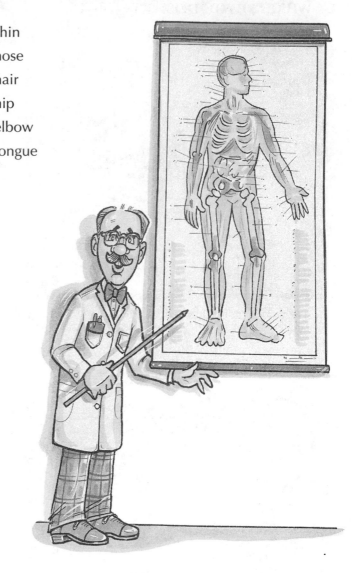

D. WHICH WORD?

1. You look different!
   I'm growing a ((beard)   nose).

2. There's a pain in my leg.
   Is it in your (shin   skin)?

3. My grandfather fell yesterday.
   Did he hurt his (mustache   hip)?

4. What's the matter with your (abdomen   chin)?
   I cut it while I was shaving.

5. I think I have a fever.
   Let me feel your (jaw   forehead).

6. Can you help me? I can't walk very well.
   When did you break your (arm   leg)?

7. I can't bend my (eyelashes   knee).
   Call your doctor.

8. I have a sore throat.
   Stick out your (lip   tongue) and say "Ah."

E. WHICH WORD DOESN'T BELONG?

1. (bones)   heart   liver   kidneys
2. palm   knuckle   veins   fingernail
3. thumb   toenail   pinky   ring finger
4. ankle   big toe   skin   heel
5. veins   knuckle   heart   arteries
6. pancreas   gallbladder   palm   lungs
7. ankle   muscle   wrist   knuckle

F. MATCHING: *ASSOCIATIONS*

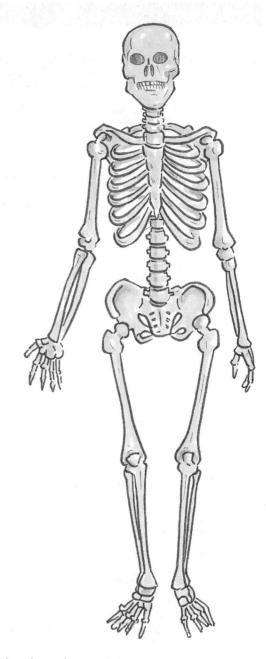

  _f_ **1.** brain   **a.** digest food
  ___ **2.** throat   **b.** point
  ___ **3.** lungs   **c.** hold
  ___ **4.** stomach   **d.** breathe
  ___ **5.** heart   **e.** swallow
  ___ **6.** hand   **f.** think
  ___ **7.** index finger   **g.** pump blood

G. MATCHING: *CLOTHING AND THE BODY*

  _e_ **1.** watch   **a.** feet
  ___ **2.** shoes   **b.** finger
  ___ **3.** gloves   **c.** neck
  ___ **4.** ring   **d.** hands
  ___ **5.** scarf   **e.** wrist

H. WHICH WORD?

1. Charles can't breathe very well.
   Did the doctor check his ((lungs) hip)?

2. Why do you think I'm nervous?
   You're biting your (muscles   fingernails).

3. My sister was in a bad accident!
   Did she break any (toenails   bones)?

4. My mother has chest pains.
   The doctor should check her (skin   heart).

5. I think I ate too much!
   Does your (stomach   spinal cord) hurt?

6. It hurts when I talk!
   I think you have a very sore (throat   thumb).

I. LISTENING: *WHAT IS IT?*

Circle the correct word.

1. thumb   (stomach)   5. chin   skin
2. eyelash   tooth   6. nose   bones
3. calf   throat   7. hip   lip
4. back   bladder   8. elbow   little toe

A. MATCHING

Match the sentences that mean the same.

_i_	**1.**	My head hurts.	**a.**	I have a backache.
___	**2.**	My throat hurts.	**b.**	I have a temperature.
___	**3.**	I hurt my back.	**c.**	I have a stomachache.
___	**4.**	My stomach feels bad.	**d.**	I have an earache.
___	**5.**	I have a fever.	**e.**	I have laryngitis.
___	**6.**	My nose is running.	**f.**	I have a sore throat.
___	**7.**	It's hard to talk.	**g.**	I have a bloody nose.
___	**8.**	My nose is bleeding.	**h.**	I have a runny nose.
___	**9.**	My skin is red and it hurts.	**i.**	I have a headache.
___	**10.**	My ear hurts.	**j.**	I have a sunburn.

B. WHAT'S THE MATTER?

sunburn	stomachache	stiff neck	chills	rash
virus	diarrhea	cavity	backache	sore throat

1. I ate candy all day. Now I have a _____ stomachache _____.

2. Barbara sat in the sun all morning. Now she has a _____.

3. I looked up in the sky all afternoon. Now I have a _____.

4. Donald feels cold. He has the _____.

5. Maria's tooth hurts when she chews food. She has a _____.

6. Bob pulled a muscle in his back. He has a _____.

7. Michael has to go to the bathroom often. He has _____.

8. My wife has a fever, the chills, and a sore throat. She has a _____.

9. Howard is scratching his skin a lot. He has a _____.

10. When Sally swallows, it hurts. She has a _____.

C. JOURNAL ENTRY

Different people and cultures have different ways to stop the hiccups. How do you stop the hiccups? How did you learn this way?

....

....

....

....

....

....

....

D. FEELING TERRIBLE

1. My grandmother fell down.
   Did she ((sprain)   burp) her ankle?

2. I feel nauseous.
   Do you think you're going to (bruise   vomit)?

3. I think I have a rash.
   Is it (itchy   bloated)?

4. My husband is sneezing and wheezing.
   He sounds (congested   swollen).

5. I twisted my knee.
   Did you (dislocate   burn) it?

6. My shoes don't fit any more!
   Are your feet (dizzy   swollen)?

7. I'm tired!
   You look (itchy   exhausted)!

8. I feel bloated.
   Try to (scrape   burp).

9. Jane fell down and hurt her knee.
   Is she (cutting   bleeding)?

10. I have a cold. I'm congested.
    Are you (twisting   coughing) a lot?

E. CROSSWORD PUZZLE

ACROSS

1.
2.

4.
6.

8.
9.

10.
11.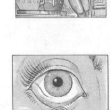

DOWN

1.
3.

5.
7.

A. MATCHING: *WHAT DO THEY DO?*

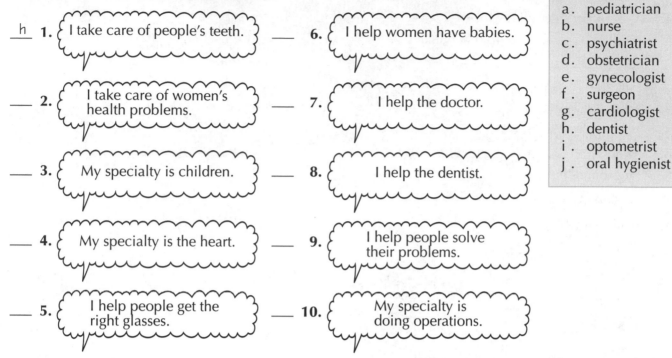

__h__ 1. { I take care of people's teeth. }

___ 2. { I take care of women's health problems. }

___ 3. { My specialty is children. }

___ 4. { My specialty is the heart. }

___ 5. { I help people get the right glasses. }

___ 6. { I help women have babies. }

___ 7. { I help the doctor. }

___ 8. { I help the dentist. }

___ 9. { I help people solve their problems. }

___ 10. { My specialty is doing operations. }

a. pediatrician
b. nurse
c. psychiatrist
d. obstetrician
e. gynecologist
f. surgeon
g. cardiologist
h. dentist
i. optometrist
j. oral hygienist

B. WHAT WILL THEY USE?

Novocaine	X-ray machine	stethoscope	examination table
thermometer	blood pressure gauge	eye chart	scale

1. I'll fill the cavity, but it won't hurt. I'll give you a shot of _____Novocaine_____

2. Put this _____ under your tongue.

3. What's your blood pressure? Let's use this _____.

4. Let's take a picture. Please step over here to the _____.

5. I use a _____ to listen to your heart.

6. Please sit down on the _____.

7. I'll check your vision with the _____.

8. How much do you weigh? Please step up on this _____.

C. LISTENING: *WHO'S TALKING?*

Listen to the sentences. Circle the correct answer.

1. (nurse)   psychiatrist
2. hygienist   obstetrician
3. X-ray technician optometrist
4. dentist   surgeon
5. pediatrician   obstetrician
6. cardiologist   pediatrician
7. gynecologist   cardiologist
8. lab technician   surgeon
9. X-ray technician optometrist
10. psychiatrist   lab technician

A. WHAT DID THE DOCTOR DO?

sling	cast	diet	exercise	prescription
rest	X-ray	crutches	stitches	bandaid

What did the doctor do. . .

1. . . . for your broken arm?
   He put it in a _____cast_____ and gave me a _____.

2. . . . for your weight problem?
   She gave me a _____ and told me to _____.

3. . . . for your fever?
   She gave me a _____ and told me to _____.

4. . . . for your broken leg?
   He took an _____, put it in a cast, and gave me _____.

5. . . . for the cut on your head?
   She gave me seven _____ and put on a large _____.

B. MATCHING: WHAT DO THEY DO?

_d_ **1.** psychiatrists   **a.** analyze blood tests

___ **2.** lab technicians   **b.** do surgery

___ **3.** surgeons   **c.** give injections

___ **4.** X-ray technicians   **d.** give counseling

___ **5.** nurses   **e.** take pictures

C. WHICH WORD?

1. Put on this hospital (bed (gown)).
2. You need to go on a (diet bandaid).
3. Here's (a prescription surgery) for your medicine.
4. You can change the position of the bed. Push the bed (control pan).
5. Take (physiotherapy blood tests) to make your muscles strong.
6. If you can't walk to the bathroom, use the bed (table pan).
7. The nurse will write the information on the (cast medical chart).
8. The lab technician put the (I.V. sling) in my arm.
9. Drink a lot of (gargle fluids).
10. The doctor gave me a (shot cast) in my arm.

A. SOLUTIONS

1. My throat hurts.
   Use a throat ((lozenge) syrup).
2. I'm coughing a lot.
   Take (cough   eye) drops.
3. I'm tired. I don't have any energy.
   Take (vitamins   teaspoons).
4. I have a headache.
   Take two (antacid tablets   aspirins).
5. I have a rash on my back.
   Use this (heating pad   ointment).

6. I have an upset stomach.
   Take (antacid   cold) tablets.
7. I have a stuffy nose.
   Use (decongestant spray   eye drops).
8. My muscles are sore.
   Use this (wheelchair   ointment).
9. I have a rash. It itches a lot.
   Put this (syrup   creme) on it.
10. I have a very bad headache.
    Take (vitamins   aspirin) and rest in bed.

B. WHAT'S THE MEDICINE?

Choose the correct medicine.

1. Take 1 teaspoon every 4 hours.
   a. aspirin   (b.) cough syrup
2. Use two times a day.
   a. nasal spray   b. vitamins
3. Use every night before you go to bed.
   a. eye drops   b. wheelchair
4. Put 2 tablets in a glass of water.
   a. antacid   b. cough drops
5. Use instead of soap.
   a. ice pack   b. creme
6. Take 2 caplets and rest in bed.
   a. decongestant spray   b. aspirin
7. Take 1 every day.
   a. vitamin   b. heating pad

C. LISTENING: WHAT'S THE DOSAGE?

Listen to the directions. Circle the correct answer.

1. (3 teaspoons)   6 capsules
2. 1 caplet   1 tablet
3. 2 teaspoons   2 tablespoons
4. 2 capsules   2 caplets

5. 1 pill   1 tablet
6. 1 teaspoon   1 capsule
7. 5 capsules   9 caplets
8. 7 caplets   11 tablets

A. SENDING MAIL

1. I'm going to the post office to mail a ((parcel) postmark).
2. I want to send this package (parcel post   postal clerk), please.
3. A book (of stamps   rate), please.
4. Please mail this (postcard   mailbox) at the post office.
5. I have to mail an air (mail   letter) at the post office.
6. How much is the (postmark   postage)?
7. I'm going to the post office to mail a (letter carrier   letter).
8. I have to send this parcel (mail   post).
9. Write the address on the (postal code   envelope).
10. Buy stamps from the postal clerk or the stamp (machine   postage).
11. The letter carrier forgot his mail (slot   bag).
12. Moving? Don't forget a (money order   change-of-address) form!

B. WHICH WORD DOESN'T BELONG?

1. stamp	address	postmark	(counter)
2. mail carrier	postal worker	mail truck	letter carrier
3. air mail	mail bag	registered mail	express mail
4. envelope	postcard	aerogramme	mail slot
5. postcard	scale	letter	parcel
6. money order	first class	parcel post	Priority Post
7. return address	postal code	postage	postal clerk
8. express mail	mailbox	mail truck	mail bag

C. MATCHING

Draw a line to the correct word. Then write the word on the line.

1. registered   post   _registered mail_
2. return   class   _____
3. first   carrier   _____
4. parcel   address   _____
5. letter   code   _____
6. postal   mail   _____

D. ADDRESSING AN ENVELOPE

You're writing a letter to a friend. Write your friend's address and your return address on the envelope.

A. AT THE LIBRARY

call number	author	shelves	microfilm	magazines	library card
card catalogue	title	checkout desk	librarian	assistant	periodicals

To find a book at the library, ask the _____librarian_____ [1], or look in the _____ [2]. You can look under the name of the _____ [3] or the _____ [4] of the book. Then find the _____ [5] in the left hand corner of the call card.

Many books are on the _____ [6]. There are many newspapers and _____ [7] in the _____ [8] section. You can use a special machine to find old newspapers on _____ [9].

To take a book out, give your _____ [10] to the library _____ [11] at the _____ [12].

B. MATCHING: *LIBRARY HELP*

_e_ **1.** I don't know the title or the author.

____ **2.** I don't know the meaning of this word.

____ **3.** Is there a movie about my subject?

____ **4.** I need to look at a map.

____ **5.** Where is yesterday's *Globe and Mail* newspaper?

____ **6.** I want to make a copy of this article.

____ **7.** Where can I get general information about this person?

a. An atlas is in the reference section.

b. Look in the encyclopedia.

c. The copier is on the second floor.

d. Check in the periodicals section.

e. Look in the card catalogue under the subject.

f. Look it up in the dictionary.

g. Go to the media section.

C. READING CALL CARDS

495 TAY	Taylor, Sarah F.
	Sports Around the World (c 1993)
1. Sports	

648.6 REY	Reynolds, John A.
	The Importance of English (c 1992)
1. Languages 2. English Language	

845.66 FIE	Field, T.C.
	North American Short Stories (c 1991)
1. Fiction	

1. Who is the author of *The Importance of English*? _____John A. Reynolds_____

2. What is the call number of *Sports Around the World*? _____

3. What is the title of Sarah F. Taylor's book? _____

4. What is the subject of Taylor's book? _____

5. Which book is about the subject of languages? _____

6. What year was *North American Short Stories* published? _____

7. Which book has the call number 845.66? _____

THE SCHOOL

A. AT SCHOOL

1. I'm going to the guidance office to see the ((guidance counselor)   cafeteria worker).
2. Your teacher is taking a break in the (locker room   teachers' lounge).
3. I'm going to the (cafeteria   chemistry lab) for lunch.
4. Put your books in your (locker   bleachers).
5. I'm going to practise English in the (field   language lab).
6. I'm sick. I'm going to see the (nurse   caretaker).
7. Carla likes science. She's often in the (chemistry lab   principal's office).
8. We're going to run around the (coach   track).
9. Let's get a cup of coffee in the (locker room   teachers' lounge).
10. All football players should go to the (language lab   field) for practice.

B. MATCHING: *ASSOCIATIONS*

 f 1. cafeteria worker
___ 2. driver's ed instructor
___ 3. teacher
___ 4. coach
___ 5. lunchroom monitor
___ 6. school nurse
___ 7. principal
___ 8. caretaker

a. classroom
b. gymnasium
c. cafeteria
d. office
e. cars, safety
f. food
g. cleaning
h. sickness

C. LISTENING: *WHO ARE THESE STUDENTS GOING TO SEE?*

Circle the correct word.

1. teacher   (guidance counselor)
2. caretaker   driver's ed instructor
3. principal   cafeteria worker
4. lunchroom monitor   school nurse

5. custodian   counselor
6. lunchroom monitor   assistant principal
7. caretaker   coach
8. assistant principal   cafeteria worker

75

A. WHERE DO THESE SUBJECTS BELONG?

| algebra | biology | calculus | chemistry | English |
| geometry | physics | Spanish | trigonometry | French |

Mathematics:

- _____algebra_____
- _____
- _____
- _____

Sciences:

- _____
- _____
- _____

Languages:

- _____
- _____
- _____

B. MATCHING: *ASSOCIATIONS*

_e_ **1.** grammar, literature

___ **2.** countries, mountains, rivers

___ **3.** flowers, animals

___ **4.** dates, wars, famous people

___ **5.** cooking, sewing

___ **6.** triangles, squares, circles

___ **7.** numbers, addition, subtraction

a. **geography**
b. **geometry**
c. **mathematics**
d. **biology**
e. **English**
f. **home economics**
g. **history**

C. MATCHING: *EXTRACURRICULAR ACTIVITIES*

_g_ **1.** I have to practise the violin.

___ **2.** I'm going to Spanish school now.

___ **3.** I like to sing.

___ **4.** I like to write poetry.

___ **5.** I'm president of the class.

___ **6.** I like sports.

___ **7.** I like to write about school news.

a. He's on the football team.

b. She's in the student government.

c. She works on the literary magazine.

d. She works on the school newspaper.

e. He goes to a heritage class.

f. He's in the choir.

g. He's in the orchestra.

D. LISTENING: *WHAT ARE THEY TALKING ABOUT?*

Listen to the sentences and circle the correct words.

1. (choir)	physics
2. art	school newspaper
3. geometry	English
4. driver's education	drama
5. Spanish	literary magazine
6. health	football
7. band	typing
8. history	calculus

E. CROSSWORD

ACROSS

1. 3 × 6 = 18

6. All about our bodies

7. Orchestras, bands, and choirs

8. Photographs of all students

DOWN

2. a s d f   j k l ;

3. Biology, for example

4. Musicians

5. For actors and actresses

F. JOURNAL ENTRY

In my opinion, the easiest school subject is _____ because . . . .

. . . .

. . . .

. . . .

The most difficult school subject is _____ because . . . .

. . . .

. . . .

. . . .

The most interesting school subject is _____ because . . . .

. . . .

. . . .

. . . .

DICTIONARY
pages 80–81

A. WHAT'S THE WORD?

actress	architect	artist	assembler	baker
bookkeeper	bricklayer	carpenter	cashier	chef

1. I work with money. I use a cash register. I'm a _____cashier_____.

2. Frank is a _____. He makes delicious bread.

3. Rita is a famous Hollywood _____. I saw her in a movie last weekend.

4. Mr. Hanson made the book shelves and fixed our steps. He's a good _____.

5. I draw plans for houses and buildings. I'm an _____.

6. Gloria puts parts together in a factory. She's an _____.

7. I draw and paint. I'm studying to be an _____.

8. Mike is a _____. He works on construction sites and builds walls.

9. I keep records of accounts for a business. I'm a _____.

10. My brother-in-law cooks very well. He's a _____.

B. MATCHING: *WHAT DO THEY DO?*

_f_ **1.** data processor	**a.**	delivers packages and letters
___ **2.** farmer	**b.**	writes articles for newspapers
___ **3.** firefighter	**c.**	cleans buildings
___ **4.** foreman	**d.**	takes purchases and makes change
___ **5.** courier	**e.**	grows vegetables to sell
___ **6.** hairdresser	**f.**	designs computer programs
___ **7.** butcher	**g.**	cuts and styles hair
___ **8.** journalist	**h.**	cuts and prepares meat
___ **9.** janitor	**i.**	puts out fires
___ **10.** cashier	**j.**	manages a construction crew

C. WHICH GROUP?

accountant	baker	barber	bookkeeper	bricklayer	caretaker
cashier	chef	courier	delivery person	hairdresser	housekeeper
			mason	messenger	

These people cut hair:
- _____
- _____

These people cook:
- _____
- _____

These people clean:
- _____
- _____

These people deliver:
- _____
- _____
- _____

These people work with numbers and money:
- _____accountant_____
- _____
- _____

These people build:
- _____
- _____

D. MATCHING: *COMPOUND WORDS*

Draw a line to complete the word. Then write the word on the line.

1. house   fighter   _____housekeeper_____

2. book   keeper   _____

3. brick   dresser   _____

4. fire   keeper   _____

5. hair   layer   _____

E. LISTENING: *WHAT'S THE JOB?*

Listen and circle the correct word.

1. (bus driver)   farmer

2. cashier   butcher

3. artist   journalist

4. baker   firefighter

5. barber   fisherman

6. cook   construction worker

7. hairdresser   carpenter

8. bookkeeper   actress

F. CAREER EXPLORATION

Look at pages 80–81 of the Picture Dictionary. Recommend one or more jobs for these people:

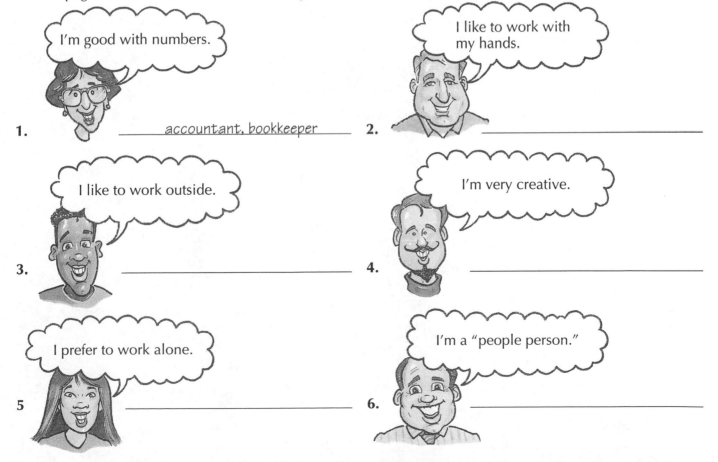

I'm good with numbers.

1. _____accountant, bookkeeper_____

I like to work with my hands.

2. _____

I like to work outside.

3. _____

I'm very creative.

4. _____

I prefer to work alone.

5 _____

I'm a "people person."

6. _____

A. JOBS

mechanic	newscaster	pharmacist	photographer	real estate agent
sanitation worker	police officer	plumber	receptionist	pilot

1. I like to work on cars. I'm an excellent _____ mechanic _____.

2. Sam can fix the pipes in the kitchen. He's an experienced _____.

3. My sister sells houses. She's a great _____.

4. Jack studied chemistry in college. Now he's a _____.

5. I enjoy people. I work as a _____ in an office.

6. I like to take pictures. I'm a _____ for the city newspaper.

7. Maxine was a journalist. Now she's a _____ on television.

8. I fly airplanes. I'm a _____.

9. Larry collects garbage from city neighbourhoods. He's a _____.

10. I want to fight crime. Some day I want to be a _____.

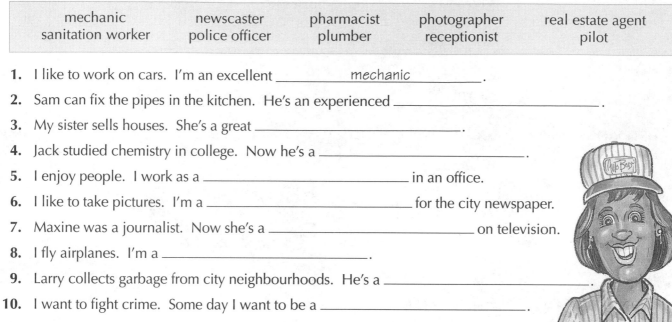

B. MATCHING: *WHERE DO THEY WORK?*

_d_ **1.** A pharmacist works   **a.** in a department store.

___ **2.** A receptionist works   **b.** in a lab.

___ **3.** A salesperson works   **c.** in a restaurant.

___ **4.** A scientist works   **d.** in a pharmacy.

___ **5.** A teacher works   **e.** in a garage or service station.

___ **6.** A waitress works   **f.** in an office.

___ **7.** A mechanic works   **g.** in a school.

C. MATCHING: *ASSOCIATIONS*

_b_ **1.** waiter   **a.** languages

___ **2.** veterinarian   **b.** food and drinks

___ **3.** translator   **c.** animals

___ **4.** seamstress   **d.** typewriters and phones

___ **5.** secretary   **e.** dresses and suits

___ **6.** photographer   **f.** cabs

___ **7.** pharmacist   **g.** garbage

___ **8.** taxi driver   **h.** pipes and water

___ **9.** sanitation worker   **i.** medicine

___**10.** plumber   **j.** camera

D. WHAT'S THE WORD?

paint	**paint*er***
interpret	interpret**er**

1. If you paint, you're a _____painter_____ .
2. If you interpret, you're an _____ .
3. If you garden, you're a _____ .
4. If you report the news, you're a _____ .
5. If you farm, you're a _____ .
6. If you drive a truck, you're a _____ .
7. If you photograph things, you're a _____ .
8. If you wait on people at a restaurant (and you're a man), you're a _____ .
9. If you weld things, you're a _____ .

E. CROSSWORD

ACROSS

1.
4.
5.
7.
8.
9.

DOWN

2.
3.
6.

WORK ACTIVITIES

A. MATCHING: *WHAT DO THEY DO?*

_e_ **1.** Bakers   **a.** draw.

___ **2.** Chefs   **b.** assemble components.

___ **3.** Assemblers   **c.** design buildings.

___ **4.** Artists   **d.** construct things.

___ **5.** Secretaries   **e.** bake.

___ **6.** Architects   **f.** cook.

___ **7.** Carpenters   **g.** file.

___ **8.** Actors   **h.** grow vegetables.

___ **9.** Construction workers   **i.** fly airplanes.

___ **10.** Pilots   **j.** act.

___ **11.** Farmers   **k.** build things.

___ **12.** Security guards   **l.** clean.

___ **13.** Truck drivers   **m.** drive trucks.

___ **14.** Housekeepers   **n.** guard buildings.

B. WHAT DO THEY DO?

1. Painters _____ *paint* _____ .

2. Repairpersons _____ .

3. Musicians _____ .

4. Waiters _____ .

5. Seamstresses and tailors _____ .

6. Teachers _____ .

7. Translators _____ .

8. Secretaries _____ .

translate
type
sew
paint
serve food
teach
fix things
play an instrument

C. WHAT'S THE WORK ACTIVITY?

bake	draw	assemble	type	grow

_____ *draw* _____   _____   _____   _____   _____

- designs
- pictures

- letters
- reports

- bread
- cookies

- components
- parts

- vegetables
- fruits

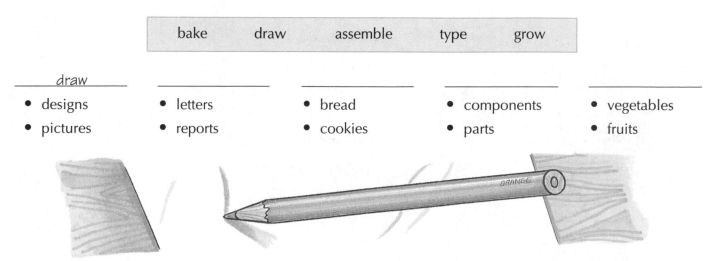

D. MATCHING: *ASSOCIATIONS*

_e_ **1.** sew
___ **2.** translate
___ **3.** mow
___ **4.** serve
___ **5.** sing
___ **6.** wash

a. dishes and clothes
b. lawns
c. food and drinks
d. languages
e. clothing
f. songs

_____

___ **7.** paint
___ **8.** type
___ **9.** fly
___ **10.** play
___ **11.** repair
___ **12.** operate

g. broken things
h. walls and houses
i. letters and reports
j. equipment and machinery
k. music
l. airplanes

E. MATCHING: *WHAT DOES IT MEAN?*

Match the words with the same meaning.

_d_ **1.** assemble components
___ **2.** mow lawns
___ **3.** operate equipment
___ **4.** repair
___ **5.** build

a. use machinery
b. fix
c. construct
d. put things together
e. cut the grass

F. LISTENING: *WHAT DO THEY DO?*

Listen and put a check next to the correct sentence.

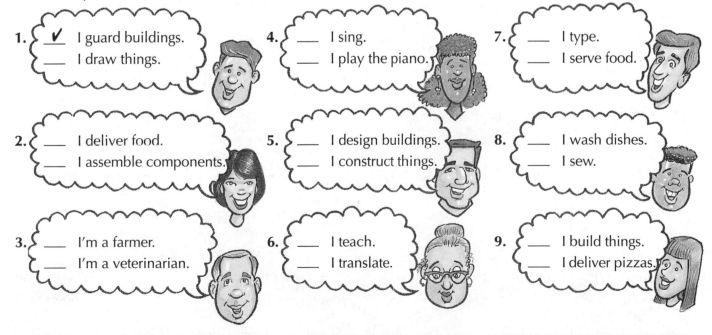

1. ✔ I guard buildings.
   ___ I draw things.

2. ___ I deliver food.
   ___ I assemble components.

3. ___ I'm a farmer.
   ___ I'm a veterinarian.

4. ___ I sing.
   ___ I play the piano.

5. ___ I design buildings.
   ___ I construct things.

6. ___ I teach.
   ___ I translate.

7. ___ I type.
   ___ I serve food.

8. ___ I wash dishes.
   ___ I sew.

9. ___ I build things.
   ___ I deliver pizzas.

A. JOE'S DAILY ROUTINE

coffee machine	workstation	coat closet	waste receptacle
mailbox	message board	typist	

Joe arrives at the office every morning at 8:30. He puts his jacket in the _____coat closet_____[1] and checks his _____[2] for any letters or information. He throws away any *junk* mail in the _____[3]. He always checks the _____[4] for any important messages. Next he goes to the _____[5] to get something to drink. Now he's ready to go to his _____[6] and begin his job as a _____[7].

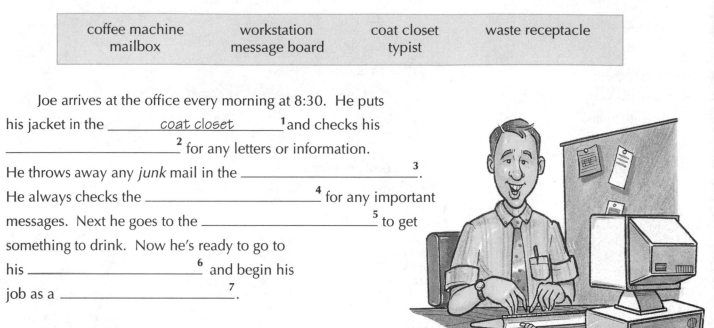

B. WHICH WORD?

1. Let's go to the ((employee lounge)   storage room) and have a cup of coffee.
2. I don't understand. I'm going to ask the (copier   boss).
3. Look in the (supply   file) cabinet for more paper and pens.
4. Someone called for you. I left his name and telephone number in your (file cabinet   mailbox).
5. Ms. Williams is the new (office manager   postage meter).
6. She's in her (office   mailbox).
7. The supplies are in the (waste receptacle   storage room).
8. The workers are at their (employee lounge   workstations).
9. A visitor in the (reception area   storage cabinet) is waiting to see Mrs. Grant.

C. MATCHING: *WHERE IS THIS CONVERSATION TAKING PLACE?*

_e_ **1.** "It's out of order again!"

___ **2.** "We'll have 20 people at this meeting."

___ **3.** "Good morning. May I help you?"

___ **4.** "I'm sending it first class."

___ **5.** "No sugar or cream. I take it black."

a. at the coffee cart

b. at the postage machine

c. in the conference room

d. in the reception area

e. at the pop machine

D. LISTENING: *WHO IS TALKING?*

Listen and circle the correct answer.

1. (file clerk)   office manager
2. boss   receptionist
3. typist   file clerk
4. administrative assistant   typist
5. receptionist   boss
6. secretary   file clerk

A. WHAT'S THE WORD?

paper shredder	phone system	plastic binding machine
fax machine	calculator	microcassette recorder

1. What's 2.6% of $2,582.80?
   I don't know. Let's use the _____calculator_____ to find the answer.

2. Can we record this meeting?
   Yes. I brought a _____.

3. Should I send this information in a letter?
   No. They need it right away. Let's use the _____.

4. Can you put all these papers together in a book?
   Yes. We have a _____.

5. There weren't any phone calls this morning.
   Maybe the _____ is broken!

6. This report is confidential. We have to destroy it.
   Don't worry. We have a _____.

B. WHICH WORD?

1. The boss bought a new laser (headset (printer)).
2. Let me show you how to use the word (processor   machine).
3. Do you know how to use the paper (sharpener   shredder)?
4. This is our new phone (machine   system).
5. I weighed the parcel on the postal (scale   machine).
6. I don't have scissors, but you can use the paper (printer   cutter).

C. MATCHING: ASSOCIATIONS

_e_ 1. telephone   a. mail
___ 2. paper shredder   b. computer
___ 3. VDT   c. numbers
___ 4. adding machine   d. trash
___ 5. postal scale   e. message

D. LISTENING: WHAT ARE THEY TALKING ABOUT?

Listen and circle the correct words.

1. (fax machine)   adding machine   4. dictaphone   telephone
2. computer   calculator   5. telex machine   pencil sharpener
3. paper shredder   paper cutter   6. postal scale   phone system

A. WHICH GROUP?

clerical	highlighter	appointment book	mechanical pencil
posture	organizer	swivel	timesheet

Types of chairs:

- _____ clerical _____
- _____
- _____

Things we write with:

- _____
- _____

Things we write in or on:

- _____
- _____
- _____

B. MATCHING: *ASSOCIATIONS*

b **1.** rolodex

___ **2.** eraser

___ **3.** pen

___ **4.** paycheque

___ **5.** desk calendar

___ **6.** wastebasket

___ **7.** punch

___ **8.** scissors

a. money

b. names and telephone numbers

c. date

d. holes

e. waste paper

f. cut

g. mistake

h. ink

C. ANALOGIES

staple remover	stamp pad	highlighter pen	pencils	typewriter

1. pencil : eraser *as* _____ typewriter _____ : correction fluid

2. memos : memo holder *as* _____ : pencil cup

3. swivel chair : chair *as* _____ : pen

4. eraser : pencil *as* _____ : stapler

5. personal planner : organizer *as* _____ : ink pad

D. WHICH WORD?

1. Where's my mechanical (eraser (pencil))?

2. Let me check my wall (pad   calendar).

3. I can't find my appointment (cards   book)!

4. I left your letter (opener   stamp) next to your mail.

5. How do you like your new file (desk   cabinet)?

6. My letter (remover   tray) is such a mess!

7. How do you put a new tape in the tape (wastebasket   dispenser)?

8. I have the rubber stamp, but I can't find the (desk   ink) pad.

A. WHICH WORD?

1.

I made a mistake on this letter. Do you have the (rubber cement (correction fluid))?

2. Don't staple the papers together. Use this (paper clip   sealing tape).

3. Write the telephone number on this (note pad   typewriter ribbon).

4. Please address this (thumbtack   mailing label).

5. The copier is broken. Please use (carbon paper   stationery) when you type the letter so we have an extra copy.

6. After you use the 3-hole punch, use three (paper fasteners   pushpins).

7. The gluestick doesn't work. Try some (typewriter ribbon   rubber cement).

8. Type this letter on our new (clamp   stationery).

9. We don't have any more mailers. Use a (mailing label   marker) and put it on a clasp envelope.

10. I need a (manila folder   catalogue envelope) to start a new file.

B. WHICH WORD?

1. Write the names of all employees on this ((legal) message) pad.

2. Hold all 50 timesheets together with a (binder   plastic) clip.

3. Do you know how to put the (computer   carbon) paper in the dot-matrix printer?

4. Write the name and telephone number on this small (legal   Post-It note) pad.

5. Masking tape isn't strong enough. Use this (cellophane   sealing) tape to send this package.

6. We're out of stationery. I have to use (typing   carbon) paper for this letter.

C. MATCHING: *WHAT DO WE USE IT FOR?*

_d_ **1.** paper clip

___ **2.** computer paper

___ **3.** message pad

___ **4.** correction fluid

___ **5.** pushpin

___ **6.** rubber cement

___ **7.** envelope

___ **8.** mailing label

___ **9.** carbon paper

a. to attach paper to a bulletin board

b. to glue pieces of paper together

c. to make a copy

d. to hold papers together

e. to cover a mistake

f. to write down messages

g. to print out information

h. to send a letter in the mail

i. to put an address on an envelope

D. LISTENING: *TAKING A MESSAGE*

Listen to the telephone conversations. Write the messages.

1.

To ___Mr. Taylor___

Date _____ Time _____ ☐ AM ☐ PM

WHILE YOU WERE OUT

M ___rs. Perez___

of _____

Phone __(905) 986-3098__

Area Code   Number   Extension

TELEPHONED	✔	PLEASE CALL	✔
CALLED TO SEE YOU		WILL CALL AGAIN	
WANTS TO SEE YOU		URGENT	
	RETURNED YOUR CALL		

Message _____

_____Call back today._____

_____

_____

_____

_____

Operator

2.

To ___Mr. Franco___

Date _____ Time _____ ☐ AM ☐ PM

WHILE YOU WERE OUT

M ___r. White___

of _____

Phone __(   )__

Area Code   Number   Extension

TELEPHONED		PLEASE CALL	
CALLED TO SEE YOU		WILL CALL AGAIN	
WANTS TO SEE YOU		URGENT	
	RETURNED YOUR CALL		

Message _____

_____

_____

_____

_____

_____

Operator

3.

To ___Mrs. Ling___

Date _____ Time _____ ☐ AM ☐ PM

WHILE YOU WERE OUT

M ___r. Ling___

of _____

Phone __(   )__

Area Code   Number   Extension

TELEPHONED		PLEASE CALL	
CALLED TO SEE YOU		WILL CALL AGAIN	
WANTS TO SEE YOU		URGENT	
	RETURNED YOUR CALL		

Message _____

_____

_____

_____

_____

_____

Operator

4.

To ___Ms. Benson___

Date _____ Time _____ ☐ AM ☐ PM

WHILE YOU WERE OUT

M ___rs. Hobbs___

of _____

Phone __(   )__

Area Code   Number   Extension

TELEPHONED		PLEASE CALL	
CALLED TO SEE YOU		WILL CALL AGAIN	
WANTS TO SEE YOU		URGENT	
	RETURNED YOUR CALL		

Message _____

_____

_____

_____

_____

_____

Operator

A. WHICH WORD?

1. I smell smoke!

Get the ((fire extinguisher) time cards)!

2. I'm thirsty, but the cafeteria is closed.

Let's get a drink from the (supply room   vending machine).

3. These boxes are very heavy.

Use the (forklift   lever).

4. There's an accident on the second floor!

Get the (first-aid kit   quality control supervisor)!

5. I have a problem with my paycheque.

Talk to the secretary in the (suggestion box   payroll office).

6. Where are the safety glasses?

In the (freight elevator   supply room).

7. I'm here for an interview.

Go to the (loading dock   personnel office) on the second floor.

8. I have a question about my job.

Ask your (foreman   worker).

9. I'm going home.

Did you punch out your time (card   clock)?

10. The food in the cafeteria is terrible!

Write a note and put it in the (suggestion box   assembly line).

B. MATCHING: *FINISH THE WORDS*

_c_ **1.** union	**a.** belt		___ **6.** loading	**f.** glasses
___ **2.** work	**b.** box		___ **7.** supply	**g.** extinguisher
___ **3.** suggestion	**c.** notice		___ **8.** assembly	**h.** room
___ **4.** conveyor	**d.** truck		___ **9.** fire	**i.** dock
___ **5.** hand	**e.** station		___ **10.** safety	**j.** line

C. WHICH WORD?

1. You can get a sandwich from the vending ((machine) box).

2. Load these boxes on the freight (elevator   machine).

3. The hand truck is at the shipping (dock   department).

4. The new employee is working at the loading (office   dock).

5. Take your time card to the personnel (department   office).

D. MATCHING: *DEFINITIONS*

_c_ **1.** time card	**a.** contains chemicals to put out fires
___ **2.** safety glasses	**b.** takes shipments up and down floors
___ **3.** worker	**c.** shows when the employee arrives and leaves
___ **4.** fire extinguisher	**d.** protects the eyes of the worker
___ **5.** first-aid kit	**e.** has bandages and bandaids
___ **6.** payroll office	**f.** is an employee
___ **7.** freight elevator	**g.** keeps paycheques for workers

A. WHICH GROUP?

brick	bulldozer	cement	crane	lumber	jackhammer
pickax	pickup truck	plywood	shovel	van	sledgehammer

Vehicles:

- _____
- _____
- _____
- _____

Tools:

- _____
- _____
- _____
- _____

Building materials:

- _____ brick _____
- _____
- _____
- _____

B. WHICH WORD?

1. Use that ((wheelbarrow)   scaffolding) to move the bricks!
2. Put on your (shingle   helmet) before you go to the construction site.
3. We don't have enough (level   plywood) to finish the job.
4. Please give me that (trowel   trailer).
5. Study the (blueprints   toolbelt) before you start the job.
6. Be careful when you come down the (ladder   shovel).
7. Are we going to have enough (sledgehammers   shingles) for the roof?
8. He operates that (bulldozer   girder) very well.

C. MATCHING: *COMPOUND WORDS*

Draw a line to the correct word. Then write the word on the line.

1. back   ax   _____ backhoe _____
2. blue   dozer   _____
3. bull   belt   _____
4. pick   prints   _____
5. sledge   hammer   _____
6. tool   hoe   _____
7. wheel   barrow   _____

D. LISTENING: *WHAT ARE THEY TALKING ABOUT?*

Listen and circle the correct word.

1. (beam)   brick
2. shovel   trowel
3. van   crane
4. blueprints   cement mixer
5. wheelbarrow   backhoe
6. level   trailer
7. girder   tape measure
8. cherry picker   shingle
9. bulldozer   front-end loader
10. insulation   tape measure
11. hardhats   pickax
12. pipe   wire

A. MATCHING: *WHAT SHOULD THEY USE?*

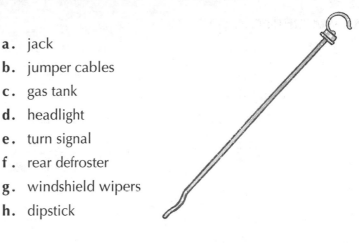

_h_ 1. "Check the oil, please."

___ 2. "It's starting to rain."

___ 3. "I have to change the tire!"

___ 4. "Make a right."

___ 5. "Fill it up."

___ 6. "It's getting dark."

___ 7. "My battery is dead!"

___ 8. "I can't see out the back of the car!"

a. jack

b. jumper cables

c. gas tank

d. headlight

e. turn signal

f. rear defroster

g. windshield wipers

h. dipstick

B. MATCHING: *COMPOUND WORDS*

Draw a line to finish the word. Then write the word on the line.

1. tail   stick   _tailpipe_ _____

2. head   cap   _____

3. hub   light   _____

4. sun   shield   _____

5. dash   pipe   _____

6. dip   roof   _____

7. wind   board   _____

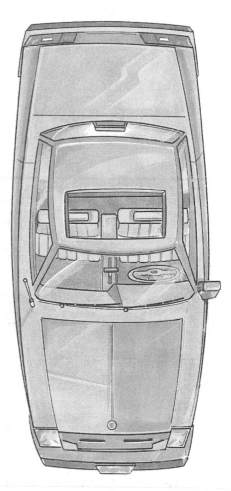

C. WHICH WORD?

1. Put on your turn (light (signal)).

2. Look in your side (pump   mirror) before you pass.

3. Your licence (rack   plate) is falling off!

4. There's a problem with your fan (filter   belt).

5. I have a spare (tire   tank) in my trunk.

6. My windshield (rear   wipers) aren't working.

7. You need oil. Look at this (dipstick   muffler).

8. Be safe. Put your (tailpipe   seat belt) on.

D. WHICH WORD?

1. The sun is bright. I can't see very well!
   Put the ((visor)   accelerator) down.

2. The light is green! Why doesn't that driver go?
   Honk your (vent   horn).

3. I can't start the car.
   I think the (ignition   brake) is broken.

4. Did you buy a car with an automatic transmission?
   No. I prefer a car with a (stickshift   headrest).

5. Where can I find a map?
   Look in the (glove compartment   shoulder harness).

6. I need help. My car broke down.
   I'll send a (limousine   tow truck).

E. MATCHING: *ASSOCIATIONS*

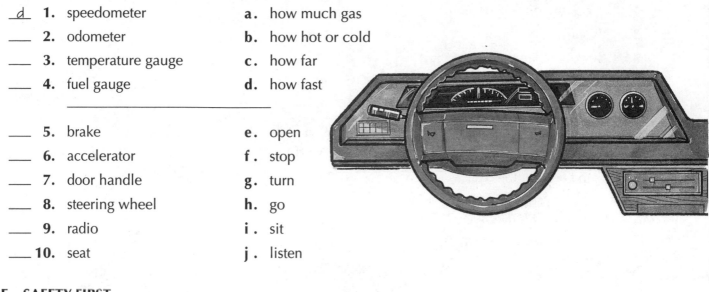

_d_ **1.** speedometer   **a.** how much gas

___ **2.** odometer   **b.** how hot or cold

___ **3.** temperature gauge   **c.** how far

___ **4.** fuel gauge   **d.** how fast

___ **5.** brake   **e.** open

___ **6.** accelerator   **f.** stop

___ **7.** door handle   **g.** turn

___ **8.** steering wheel   **h.** go

___ **9.** radio   **i.** sit

___ **10.** seat   **j.** listen

F. SAFETY FIRST

air bags	flares	jack	jumper cables	seat belts	spare tire	trunk

As a good driver, you should always keep emergency equipment in the ___trunk___[1] of your car. When your battery doesn't work, you need to use _____[2] and get help from another driver. In case of an emergency on the road, you can warn other drivers when you light your _____[3] and put them on the street. When you have a flat tire, pull over. Make sure you stop in a safe area. Use your _____[4] to lift your car. Replace the flat tire with a _____[5]. You and your passengers should always use your _____[6]. Some cars have _____[7] to protect people in an accident.

G. LISTENING: *CHECKLIST*

Listen to the car dealers. Put a check next to the items each car has.

1.
- ✔ sunroof
- ___ luggage carrier
- ___ jack
- ___ spare tire
- ___ side mirror
- ___ cruise control
- ___ rear defroster
- ___ air bag
- ___ tape deck

2.
- ___ sunroof
- ___ luggage carrier
- ___ jack
- ___ spare tire
- ___ side mirror
- ___ cruise control
- ___ rear defroster
- ___ air bag
- ___ tape deck

A. WHICH WORD?

1. You didn't stop at the (route (stop)) sign.
2. You can get off the highway at the next (entrance   exit) ramp.
3. Make a right turn at the next (shoulder   intersection).
4. The (speed limit   yield) sign says 90.
5. There's a (median   crosswalk) at the next intersection.
6. We can buy gasoline at the (school crossing   service area).
7. Pay 25¢ at the (barrier   tollbooth).
8. Meet me at the (overpass   corner) of Pearson Avenue and Elm Street.

B. MATCHING: *ASSOCIATIONS*

_f_ **1.** tollbooth
___ **2.** broken line
___ **3.** exit sign
___ **4.** solid line
___ **5.** entrance ramp
___ **6.** crosswalk

a. You can pass.
b. You can walk here.
c. You get on here.
d. You can't pass.
e. You get off here.
f. You pay here.

C. WHAT ARE THEY TALKING ABOUT?

| speed limit sign   tunnel   yield sign   snowplough   school crossing   service area |

1. "Slow down. Watch for children." ___school crossing___
2. "Get some gas. Check the oil." _____
3. "Slow down. Look carefully before you continue." _____
4. "I'm pleased it's clearing the road." _____
5. "Don't go so fast!" _____
6. "Turn your lights on before you enter." _____

D. JOURNAL ENTRY

You witnessed an accident! The insurance company wants you to describe what happened. Draw a diagram and tell about the accident.

· ·
· ·
· ·
· ·
· ·

E. LISTENING: *TRAFFIC SIGNS*

Listen to the conversations. Write the number under the correct sign.

___   ___   _1_   ___   ___

A. WHERE DID THEY GO?

arrival and departure board	information booth	luggage	platform	porter
ticket window	timetable	track	train station	train

When we arrived at the _____ train station _____ [1], we first
went to the _____ [2] to get a _____ [3]
to see when the trains left. We decided to take the next _____ [4] to Montreal.
We bought our tickets at the _____ [5]. According to
the _____ [6], our train was going to depart at 2:15 on
_____ [7] 18. It was 2:05! A _____ [8]
carried our _____ [9] from the ticket window to the
_____ [10], and we got on the train.

We were on our way to Montreal!

B. WHICH WORD DOESN'T BELONG?

1. engineer   bus driver   (turnstile)   cab driver
2. token   passenger   commuter   rider
3. ticket   sleeper   token   fare card
4. track   bus stop   taxi stand   engine
5. sleeper   dining car   passenger car   porter
6. porter   conductor   transfer   passenger

C. WHICH WORD?

1. We're going to be riding all night. Let's get a ((sleeper)   platform).
2. How much is the (meter   fare) to the train station?
3. Don't leave the luggage on the (platform   transfer).
4. My aunt is going to meet us at the (engine   bus station).
5. The departure times are in the (turnstile   timetable).
6. Pay at the (information   token) booth.
7. The (engineer   porter) will carry your baggage.
8. There was a line of passengers at the ticket (box   counter).

D. LISTENING: WHERE ARE THEY?

Listen to the conversations and decide where the passengers are.

___ on the train	___ in a subway station	___ in the dining car
___ in a taxi	__1__ on a bus	___ at an information booth

A. WHICH WORD?

1. Show your ticket to the agent at the ((check-in counter) concession stand).
2. Let me help you with that (gate suitcase).
3. All passengers have to go through the (metal detector baggage carousel).
4. May I see your (ticket counter boarding pass)?
5. Please take a seat in the (waiting area check-in counter).
6. The (customs officer porter) will take your baggage to the ticket counter.
7. Please fill out your customs (declaration form officer).
8. May I carry your (garment bag porter)?

B. WHICH WORD DOESN'T BELONG?

1. ticket agent   (luggage carrier)   security guard   customs officer
2. immigration   baggage   suitcase   luggage
3. ticket   boarding pass   X-ray machine   claim check
4. X-ray machine   metal detector   baggage carousel   security guard
5. concession stand   gift shop   snack bar   immigration
6. ticket   gate   passport   visa

C. A TICKET

PASSENGER TICKET AND BAGGAGE CHECK
NOT TRANSFERABLE

FLIGHT COUPON XXXXX   AGENT CODE A39668005   NAME OF PASSENGER JOHNSON/JAMES
ISSUED BY AIR CANADA   PLACE OF ISSUE TORONTO   DATE OF ISSUE 12 MAY   FROM TORONTO
NAME OF PASSENGER JOHNSON/JAMES   PHR/CARRIER CODE AC/AA   SERV CARR ID 0011/   TO MADRID
X/O FROM TORONTO   CARRIER AC   FLIGHT 723   CLASS V   DATE 05JUL   TIME 505PM*****   CARRIER AIR CANADA
X/O TO MADRID   ISSUING AGENT ID EE60AB5   CARR FL CL DATE TIME AC 723 V 05JUL 505P
SEAT 16D   SMOKE NO   GATE   SEAT 16D   SMOKE NO
FARE/CND$ 778.00***************   ******
TAX 26.00****43551203146   CPN   DOCUMENT NUMBER   CK
TOTAL 804.00***************   NOT VALID WITHOUT FLIGHT COUPON ATTACHED
PCS WT UNCKD BAGGAGE ID # ******************* ******************* AA39668005

1. What is the passenger's name?   *James Johnson*
2. Which airline is this passenger traveling on?
3. What is the date of departure?
4. What is the time of departure?
5. What city does the flight leave from?
6. Where is the passenger going?
7. What is the flight number?
8. How much does the ticket cost?
9. On what date did the passenger buy the ticket?

A. WHAT DO THEY NEED?

1. I feel nauseous. I think I'm going to be sick.

   Here. Use this (oxygen mask (air sickness bag)).

2. How do I move my seat back?

   Use the (seat control   armrest).

3. Where can I wash my hands?

   The (lavatory   runway) is in the back of the plane.

4. Where can I put this carry-on bag?

   You can put it in the (overhead compartment   instrument panel).

5. I'm having trouble breathing!

   Put on this (galley   oxygen mask) and breathe slowly.

6. I'm looking for our flight attendant.

   I just saw him in the (seat pocket   galley).

B. WHICH WORD?

1. The co-pilot knows all the parts of the instrument ((panel)   instruction).
2. The sign says to fasten your seat (pocket   belt).
3. Where is the emergency (compartment   exit)?
4. The plane will taxi to the terminal (tower   building).
5. The pilot put down the landing (control   gear).
6. The captain and co-pilot sit in the (engine   nose) of the plane.

C. MATCHING: WHAT IS IT?

_d_	**1.** terminal	**a.**	the bathroom
___	**2.** nose	**b.**	the captain
___	**3.** landing gear	**c.**	the motor
___	**4.** lavatory	**d.**	the main building
___	**5.** jet	**e.**	the wheels
___	**6.** engine	**f.**	the front of the plane
___	**7.** tail	**g.**	the airplane
___	**8.** pilot	**h.**	the end of the plane

D. LISTENING

Listen and check the words you hear.

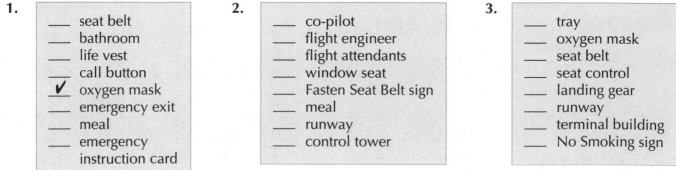

1.
___ seat belt
___ bathroom
___ life vest
___ call button
✔ oxygen mask
___ emergency exit
___ meal
___ emergency
instruction card

2.
___ co-pilot
___ flight engineer
___ flight attendants
___ window seat
___ Fasten Seat Belt sign
___ meal
___ runway
___ control tower

3.
___ tray
___ oxygen mask
___ seat belt
___ seat control
___ landing gear
___ runway
___ terminal building
___ No Smoking sign

A. WHAT'S THE WORD?

snowing	foggy	raining	clear	windy

1. Take an umbrella. It's _____raining_____ .
2. Be careful when you drive home. It's hard to see because it's so _____ .
3. It's cold! I think it will be _____ soon.
4. There isn't a cloud in the sky. It's a _____ blue sky!
5. The leaves are blowing off the trees. It's really _____ !

B. MATCHING: *ASSOCIATIONS*

_c_ **1.** snowstorm   **a.** flashes of light in the sky

___ **2.** lightning   **b.** very strong winds and rain

___ **3.** thunderstorm   **c.** cold winds and snow

___ **4.** hurricane   **d.** warm rain and noises in the sky

___ **5.** winter   **e.** flowers bloom

___ **6.** spring   **f.** leaves fall

___ **7.** summer   **g.** cold temperatures

___ **8.** autumn   **h.** hot temperatures

C. FAHRENHEIT AND CELSIUS

Look at the thermometer on page 98 of the Picture Dictionary. Read the sentence and choose the correct temperature.

1. "It's very hot today."   (**a.**) 30°C   **b.** 13°C
2. "It's very cold outside."   **a.** 15°C   **b.** -15°C
3. "It's a nice warm day."   **a.** 70°F   **b.** 17°F
4. "It's snowing."   **a.** -5°C   **b.** 5°C
5. "It's very hot today!"   **a.** 40°F   **b.** 40°C
6. "What a big snowstorm!"   **a.** 10°F   **b.** 10°C

D. LISTENING: *WEATHER FORECASTS*

Listen and write the number under the correct picture.

 ___1___   _____   _____   _____

OUTDOOR RECREATION

A. WHICH WORD?

1. We're going to be here all night. Did you bring your sleeping ((bag) boots)?
2. Where's the picnic (blanket   basket) for our drinks and sandwiches?
3. Let's put up the tent. Where are the (thermos   stakes)?
4. I don't want to get lost. Bring the compass and the (trail map   harness).
5. It's getting dark. Did you bring the (lantern   hatchet)?
6. I'm thirsty. Do you have the (compass   thermos)?
7. I can carry supplies in this (backpack   sleeping bag).
8. Hold on to the (rope   compass) with both hands.

B. MATCHING

_b_	**1.** hiking	**a.**	going up
___	**2.** on a picnic	**b.**	walking
___	**3.** climbing	**c.**	sleeping outside
___	**4.** camping	**d.**	eating
___	**5.** backpack	**e.**	cooking
___	**6.** hatchet	**f.**	light
___	**7.** lantern	**g.**	carrying
___	**8.** camp stove	**h.**	chopping

C. MATCHING

_d_	**1.** picnic	**a.**	bag
___	**2.** hiking	**b.**	stakes
___	**3.** trail	**c.**	boots
___	**4.** camp	**d.**	basket
___	**5.** tent	**e.**	stove
___	**6.** sleeping	**f.**	map

D. LISTENING: *WHERE ARE THEY GOING?*

Listen and write the number next to the correct word.

___ camping   ___ hiking   _1_ rock climbing   ___ on a picnic

THE PARK AND THE PLAYGROUND

A. WHICH WORD?

1. I'm going to get a drink at the (wading pool (water fountain)).
2. Let's go see the animals (at the zoo   on the monkey bars).
3. Put your bike (on the grill   in the bike rack).
4. I'm going to run on the (merry-go-round   jogging path).
5. Please throw this away in the (sandbox   garbage can).
6. Look at the horses on the (jungle gym   bridle path).
7. There is music every evening at the (washrooms   band shell).
8. We can cook our food on the (grill   swings).

B. ANALOGIES

| jogging path | tire swing | duck pond | washroom | bridle path | sandbox |

1. water : wading pool *as* sand : _____ sandbox _____
2. bicycle : bikeway *as* horse : _____
3. animals : zoo *as* ducks : _____
4. merry-go-round : carousel *as* lavatory : _____
5. horses : bridle path *as* people : _____
6. sit : bench *as* swing: _____

C. WHAT ARE THEY TALKING ABOUT?

| statue | seesaw | bench | water fountain | duck pond | jungle gym | picnic area | zoo |

1. "Don't climb up there so high!" _____ jungle gym _____
2. "Be careful! Don't fall in!" _____
3. "Take a drink!" _____
4. "Up and down! Up and down!" _____
5. "Sit down here and rest for a minute!" _____
6. "Let's stop and eat here!" _____
7. "Look at all the animals!" _____
8. "Who's that?" _____

D. LISTENING: *WHAT ARE THEY TALKING ABOUT?*

Listen and circle the correct word.

1. (jungle gym)   wading pool
2. garbage can   washroom
3. playground   merry-go-round
4. picnic area   bikeway
5. bike rack   sandbox
6. fountain   duck pond
7. trash can   sand
8. carousel   band shell

A. MATCHING: *WHAT DO THEY DO?*

_c_ **1.** lifeguard   **a.** sells drinks and snacks

___ **2.** surfer   **b.** sits in the sun

___ **3.** vendor   **c.** saves swimmers

___ **4.** sunbather   **d.** rides the waves

___ **5.** sunglasses   **e.** keeps hair dry

___ **6.** cooler   **f.** protect the eyes

___ **7.** bathing cap   **g.** protects the skin

___ **8.** sunscreen   **h.** keeps drinks cold

B. WHICH WORD?

1. When I'm at the beach, I always sit under a ((beach umbrella) cooler).

2. The sun is very bright! I need my (sand castle   sunglasses).

3. It's really windy! What a good day to fly a (surfboard   kite)!

4. Let's sit down on this (shovel   blanket).

5. I'm going to the (sand dune   refreshment stand) to get a drink.

6. Let's throw the (beach ball   snack bar) around.

7. I bought a new (swimsuit   rock).

8. Use a (bucket   towel) to make a sand castle.

9. The lifeguard is a very strong (sunbather   swimmer).

10. The surfers are happy about the big (pails   waves).

C. ANALOGIES

raft	wave	lifeguard stand	kite	bathing cap	swimsuit

1. sunbather : sun hat *as* swimmer : _____ bathing cap _____

2. pail : bucket *as* bathing suit : _____

3. wave : surfboard *as* wind : _____

4. sunbather : beach chair *as* lifeguard : _____

5. seashell : shell *as* air mattress : _____

6. sand : dune *as* water : _____

D. LISTENING: *WHAT ARE THEY TALKING ABOUT?*

1. (chair)   shovel   **5.** swimsuit   sunscreen

2. raft   kite   **6.** vendor   surfer

3. tube   bathing cap   **7.** blanket   sun hat

4. shovel   towel   **8.** life preserver   sunbather

A. WHAT ARE THEY?

bowling shoes	boxing gloves	darts	frisbee
handball glove	jogging shoes	walking shoes	

Things you throw:

_____

_____

Things you wear on your feet:

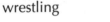 bowling shoes

_____

_____

Things you wear on your hands:

_____

_____

B. MATCHING: *ASSOCIATIONS*

<u>d</u> **1.** ping pong   **a.** glove

___ **2.** skydiving   **b.** ball

___ **3.** bowling   **c.** airplane

___ **4.** boxing   **d.** net

___ **5.** skateboarding   **e.** saddle

___ **6.** wrestling   **f.** elbow pad

___ **7.** horseback riding   **g.** mat

C. WHICH WORD?

1. Put your feet in the ((stirrups)   safety goggles).

2. Put on your (saddle   helmet) before you go biking.

3. Protect your eyes with (parachutes   safety goggles).

4. Throw the (frisbee   dart) to me!

5. Peter lifts (ping pong balls   weights) every day.

6. Kathy likes to jump on the (target   trampoline).

7. Please hand me the pool (table   stick).

8. Tom likes to practise with a bow and (ball   arrow).

9. My new wrestling (uniform   mat) doesn't fit!

10. I wear my (handball   boxing) glove on my left hand.

D. ANALOGIES

archery	billiard balls	skydiving	roller skating	golf club	paddle

1. squash ball : squash racquet *as* ping pong ball : _____ paddle _____

2. tennis ball : golf ball *as* tennis racquet : _____

3. elbow pads : skateboarding *as* knee pads : _____

4. dartboard : darts *as* target : _____

5. trampoline : gymnastics *as* parachute : _____

6. tennis : tennis balls *as* pool : _____

A. WHICH SPORTS?

Look carefully at the pictures on page 104 of the Picture Dictionary and answer the questions.

1. In which sports do players wear something on their heads?

    _____baseball_____   _____   _____

    _____   _____

2. Which sport uses a ball that isn't round? _____

3. Which sports are played on a field?

    _____   _____   _____

    _____   _____

4. Which sport is played on a rink? _____

B. CROSSWORD

ACROSS

1.
4.
5.
6.

DOWN

2.
3.

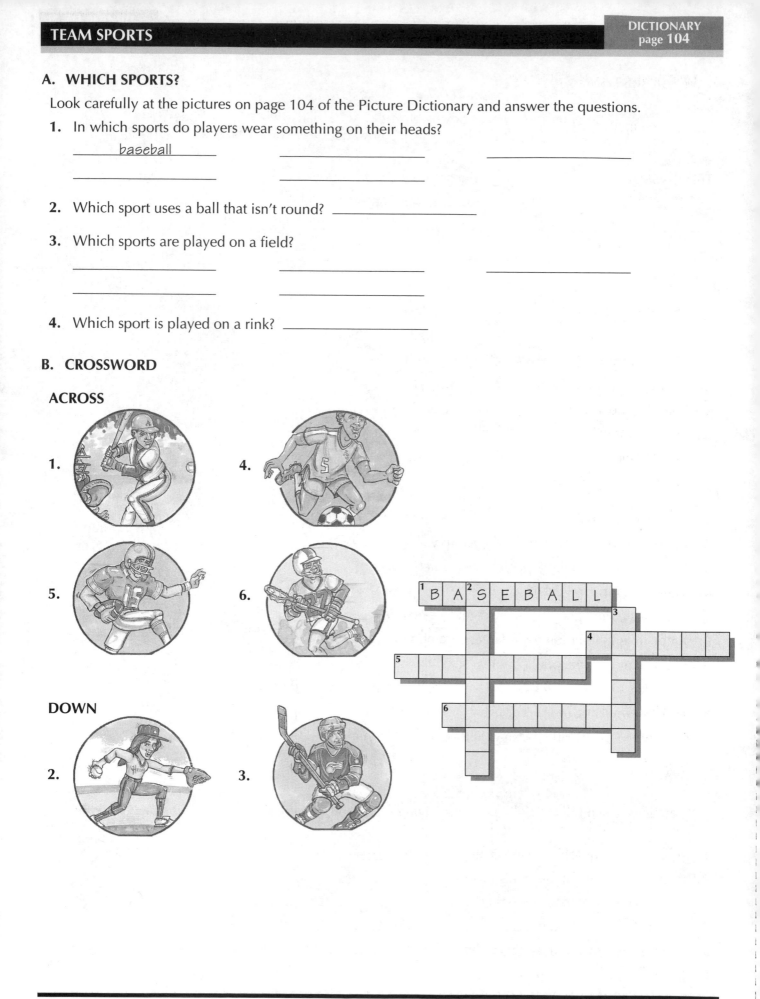

TEAM SPORTS EQUIPMENT

A. MATCHING: ASSOCIATIONS

_e_ **1.** softball

___ **2.** football

___ **3.** hockey

___ **4.** soccer

___ **5.** volleyball

___ **6.** lacrosse

___ **7.** basketball

___ **8.** baseball

a. skates, stick, mask

b. hoop, backboard

c. face guard, stick, ball

d. shinguards, goal

e. glove, softball

f. bat, helmet, glove, mitt

g. helmet, shoulder pads

h. net, volleyball

B. WHICH WORD?

1. I'm batting next. Where's the batting (stick   (helmet))?

2. Put on the hockey (puck   mask) to protect your face.

3. That player dropped the hockey (skate   stick)!

4. The basketball went in the (glove   hoop).

5. Football players must wear (mitts   helmets).

6. I can't find my softball (glove   shinguards).

7. Hit the puck with the (hockey   lacrosse) stick.

8. All the players on our team are wearing new (uniforms   nets).

C. WHICH WORD DOESN'T BELONG?

1. catcher's mask	hockey mask	face guard	(shinguard)
2. bat	lacrosse ball	hockey puck	soccer ball
3. hockey stick	bat	backboard	lacrosse stick
4. baseball glove	shoulder pads	hockey glove	catcher's mitt
5. basketball	football	volleyball	hockey

D. LISTENING: WHICH SPORT IS IT?

Listen to the radio announcer and write the number next to the correct picture.

WINTER SPORTS AND RECREATION

A. WHICH SPORTS?

Look carefully at the pictures on page 106 of the Picture Dictionary and answer the questions.

1. For which sports do you use poles?

   <u>   downhill skiing   </u>   _____

2. Which sports do you do on ice?

   _____   _____

3. For which activity do you need gasoline for your motor? _____

4. Which sports and activities do you do sitting down?

   _____   _____

   _____   _____

B. MATCHING: *WHERE?*

<u>c</u> 1. downhill skiing   a. on an ice rink

___ 2. cross-country skiing   b. through a field or woods noisily

___ 3. skating   c. down a mountain, standing up

___ 4. sledding   d. through a field or woods quietly

___ 5. snowmobile   e. down a hill, sitting down

C. WHICH WORD?

1. We go downhill skiing without ((poles) bindings)!
2. My daughter practises figure (skating   skiing) every day.
3. We can go across the mountain easily with the (saucer   snowmobile).
4. My friends are on the Olympic (sledding   bobsledding) team.
5. Don't fall off the (toboggan   bindings)!
6. (Downhill   Cross-country) skiing is so calm and peaceful.

D. MATCHING: *DEFINITIONS*

<u>b</u> 1. We use these to protect the bottom of skates.   a. saucer

___ 2. We use these to attach ski boots to skis.   b. skate guards

___ 3. This is a round type of sled.   c. poles

___ 4. This is a vehicle with a motor.   d. bindings

___ 5. We use these to help us keep balance.   e. snowmobile

WATER SPORTS AND RECREATION

A. WHICH WORD?

1. The waves are big! Get your (snorkel (surfboard))!
2. The towrope broke while I was (figure skating   waterskiing).
3. I need some bait before I go (sailing   fishing).
4. Do you have your (mask   oars) for snorkeling?
5. I always go (surfing   fishing) in this pond.
6. Use this life preserver when you go (scuba diving   sailing).

B. MATCHING: *ASSOCIATIONS*

_d_ **1.** goggles   **a.** feet
___ **2.** snorkel   **b.** chest
___ **3.** flippers   **c.** head
___ **4.** life jacket   **d.** eyes
___ **5.** bathing cap   **e.** mouth

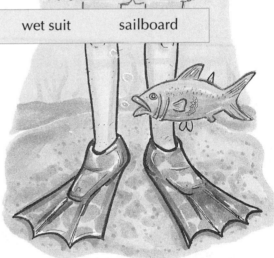

C. ANALOGIES

| flippers | swimsuit | air tank | paddles | wet suit | sailboard |

1. oars : rowboat *as* _____paddles_____ : canoe
2. waterskis : waterskiing *as* _____ : windsurfing
3. bathing suit : swimming *as* _____ : scuba diving
4. goggles : eyes *as* _____ : feet
5. snorkel : snorkeling *as* _____ : scuba diving
6. wet suit : diving mask *as* _____ : goggles

D. LISTENING: *WHAT ARE THEY DOING?*

Listen and write the number under the correct picture.

___

___

___

__1__

___

___

SPORT AND EXERCISE ACTIONS

A. WHICH WORD?

1. Can you ((bend) shoot) your knee?
2. He can (lift pass) the football very far!
3. (Dribble Reach) the ball!
4. (Lie down Dive) into the deep part of the pool.
5. (Shoot Push) the arrow from the bow.
6. Let's (run catch) around the jogging path.
7. Before you exercise, (stretch bounce) your legs.
8. (Jump Swing) your arms up and down.
9. (Hit Throw) the ball with the bat.
10. (Hop Kneel) on your right foot ten times.

B. ANALOGIES

kneel	hop	baseball	hands	shoot	throw

1. hit : baseball *as* _____shoot_____ : basketball
2. kick : soccer *as* _____ : baseball
3. tennis : serve *as* _____ : pitch
4. feet : hop *as* _____ : cartwheel
5. walk: run *as* _____ : jump
6. reach : hands *as* _____ : knees

C. MATCHING: *ASSOCIATIONS*

_e_ **1.** kick   **a.** tennis

___ **2.** pitch   **b.** basketball

___ **3.** shoot   **c.** volleyball

___ **4.** pass   **d.** baseball

___ **5.** serve   **e.** football

D. LISTENING: *AEROBICS*

Listen and put the number under the correct picture.

____   ____   ____   1   ____   ____

A. WHAT'S THE WORD?

| pottery | astronomy | sewing | coin collecting |
| painting | games | photography | woodworking |

1. My son likes to build things. His hobby is _____woodworking_____.
2. Janet takes wonderful pictures. She likes _____.
3. My mother makes all her clothes. She's very good at _____.
4. We bought David an easel. He enjoys _____.
5. The moon is clear tonight! I like _____!
6. What do you want to play? I have a lot of different _____.
7. What kind of clay do you use to make your _____?
8. My uncle has money from all over the world. He really enjoys _____.

B. MATCHING: ASSOCIATIONS

_c_ 1. knitting   **a.** bowls
___ 2. painting   **b.** clothes
___ 3. pottery   **c.** sweaters
___ 4. weaving   **d.** rugs
___ 5. sewing   **e.** pictures

C. ANALOGIES

| knitting | binoculars | bird watching | knitting needle | coin album |

1. stamps : stamp album *as* coins : _____coin album_____
2. thread : sewing *as* yarn : _____
3. crocheting : knitting *as* crochet hook : _____
4. coin catalogue : coin collecting *as* field guide : _____
5. astronomy : telescope *as* birdwatching : _____

D. WHAT ARE THEY TALKING ABOUT?

| astronomy | bird watching | coin collecting | Scrabble | sewing |

1. "It's a very rare dime. It's from 1927." _____coin collecting_____
2. "Can you see the North Star?" _____
3. "My needle broke!" _____
4. "Look at the colour of those feathers!" _____
5. "I'm not sure how to spell this word!" _____

A. WHICH WORD?

1. It was a good movie. The ((audience)   chorus) clapped at the end.
2. The (spotlight   orchestra) was on the opera singer as she sang.
3. I'll wait for you in the (refreshment stand   lobby).
4. We couldn't see well. We sat in the (podium   balcony).
5. She dances for a very good ballet (slipper   company).
6. You can get your (tickets   toeshoes) at the box office.
7. The singing of the (musicians   chorus) was wonderful.
8. The musicians followed the (baton   podium) of the conductor.

B. MATCHING

_d_ **1.** orchestra   **a.** office
___ **2.** symphony   **b.** singer
___ **3.** opera   **c.** orchestra
___ **4.** ballet   **d.** pit
___ **5.** box   **e.** dancer

C. WHICH WORD DOESN'T BELONG?

1. mezzanine   (usher)   stage   podium
2. actress   ballerina   opera singer   billboard
3. chorus   toeshoes   audience   musicians
4. ballet company orchestra   chorus   ballerina
5. balcony   ticket   mezzanine   orchestra
6. ballerina   conductor   ballet dancer dancer

D. WHO IS TALKING?

Write the correct word.

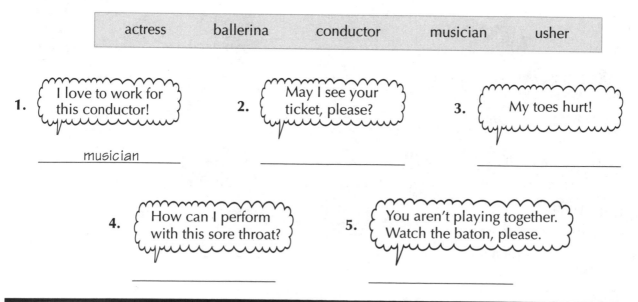

| actress | ballerina | conductor | musician | usher |

1. I love to work for this conductor!

_____musician_____

2. May I see your ticket, please?

_____

3. My toes hurt!

_____

4. How can I perform with this sore throat?

_____

5. You aren't playing together. Watch the baton, please.

_____

A. WHO LIKES WHAT?

TV programs	music	play	movies

I like to go out on Friday and Saturday nights. I like to go to concerts to listen to _____music_____ [1]
or go to the theatre to see a _____ [2].

My brother doesn't like to go out on weekends. He's happy to stay home, sit in the living room, and watch his favourite _____ [3].

My big sister likes to stay home, too. She rents _____ [4] and watches them on the VCR!

We never do anything together!

B. LISTENING: *WHAT KIND OF MUSIC?*

Listen and circle the correct words.

1. (classical music)   popular music   3. jazz   reggae
2. blues   bluegrass   4. rap music   rock music

C. WHAT TYPE OF MOVIE IS IT?

Write the correct word.

cartoon	comedy	foreign
war	western	

1. "I'm gonna get that rabbit if it's the last thing I do!"   _____cartoon_____
2. "Hey, cowboy!"   _____
3. "The enemy is here! The fighting will begin soon."   _____
4. "Non possiamo vivere cosi. Scappiamo subito."   _____
5. "Ha, ha, ha!"   _____

D. WHAT TYPE OF TV PROGRAM IS IT?

news program	game show	sports show
children's show	talk show	music video

1. "So, what's the name of your next movie?"   _____talk show_____
2. "And the winner of today's show is . . . "   _____
3. "A, B, C, D, E, F, G, . . . "   _____
4. "Good evening. This is Thursday, November 11, 1999."   _____
5. "And next, here's the latest song from Aerosmith."   _____
6. "The score is 2 to zero. . . "   _____

A. WHICH WORD DOESN'T BELONG?

1. synthesizer   (banjo)   organ   piano
2. harp   mandolin   viola   accordion
3. trumpet   bassoon   recorder   piccolo
4. guitar   ukelele   clarinet   bass
5. drum   xylophone   conga   harmonica

B. CROSSWORD

ACROSS

2.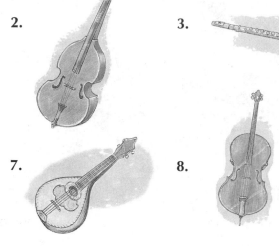

3.

7.

8.

DOWN

1.

4.

5.

6.

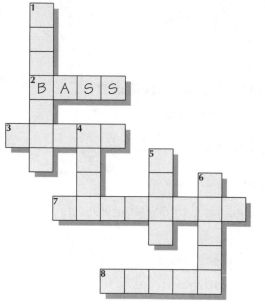

C. LISTENING: *WHICH INSTRUMENT IS IT?*

Listen and circle the correct word.

1. (viola)   trombone
2. conga   clarinet
3. trumpet   bass
4. xylophone   saxophone
5. ukelele   synthesizer
6. electric guitar   harp

A. WHAT'S THE WORD?

branch	maple	tulips	leaves	palm	grass

1. I like the different colours of ___leaves___ in the fall.
2. During the storm a big _____ from a tree fell on my car.
3. I cut the _____ every Saturday afternoon.
4. The _____ leaf is a symbol on the Canadian flag.
5. Many colourful types of _____ come from the Netherlands.
6. Look at all the coconuts on that _____ tree!

B. MATCHING: *ASSOCIATIONS*

_b_ **1.** cactus   **a.** cone
___ **2.** rose   **b.** desert
___ **3.** pine   **c.** rash
___ **4.** grass   **d.** thorn
___ **5.** poison ivy   **e.** lawnmower

C. ANALOGIES

bulb	flower	cactus
trunk	sunflower	

1. stem : flower *as* ____trunk____ : tree
2. tree : maple *as* _____ : lily
3. leaf : leaves *as* _____ : cacti
4. root : elm *as* _____ : tulip
5. flower : tree *as* _____ : redwood

D. CROSSWORD

ACROSS

1.   **2.**    **4.**

5.   **7.**

DOWN

1.   **2.**

3.   **6.**

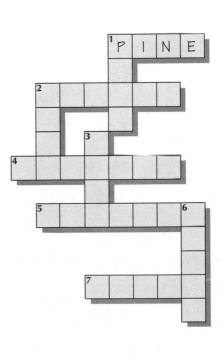

THE ENVIRONMENT AND ENERGY

A. WHICH WORD?

1. We're going to take our canoe down the (waterfall (river)).
2. Let's take a hike in the (forest   pond).
3. Do you heat your house with (oil   radiation)?
4. There's a farm in the (valley   desert) between the two mountains.
5. They went fishing in the (water pollution   brook).
6. It isn't a mountain. It's just a little (dam   hill).
7. The factory closed because of its (toxic waste   solar energy).
8. Don't go too close to the (dune   cliff)! You'll fall off!

B. WHICH WORD DOESN'T BELONG?

1. stream	brook	river	(desert)
2. meadow	rapids	field	valley
3. bay	oil	gas	coal
4. island	desert	valley	ocean
5. waterfall	pond	hill	rapids
6. toxic waste	solar energy	acid rain	water pollution
7. seashore	jungle	forest	woods

C. MATCHING: *WHAT'S THE PLACE?*

_b_ 1. a hot and dry place   a. plateau
___ 2. a place with trees and animals   b. desert
___ 3. high and flat land   c. ocean
___ 4. water with waves   d. forest
___ 5. a hill of sand   e. dune

D. MATCHING: *ASSOCIATIONS*

_d_ 1. solar energy   a. toxic waste
___ 2. hydroelectric power   b. radiation
___ 3. air pollution   c. cars
___ 4. nuclear energy   d. sunshine
___ 5. water pollution   e. waterfalls

E. JOURNAL ENTRY

List three ways people can protect the environment.

1. ....
2. ....
3. ....

A. WHICH WORD?

1. Give the horses ((hay) turkey) to eat.
2. I'm growing tomatoes, peppers, and corn in my (crop   garden).
3. Let's make a (fence   scarecrow) to keep the birds away.
4. Our garden gets enough water with our new (hired hand   irrigation system).
5. Please hand me that (orchard   pitchfork).
6. The calves are in the (farmhouse   barnyard).
7. Take the (turkeys   sheep) to the pasture.
8. We keep the supplies in the (combine   barn).

B. ANALOGIES

| calf | chicken | farmer | goat | hen | horse | piglet |

1. bull : cow *as* rooster : _____hen_____
2. hen house : chicken *as* stable : _____
3. lamb : sheep *as* kid : _____
4. pig sty : chicken coop *as* pig : _____
5. barn : farm animal *as* farmhouse : _____
6. chicken : chick *as* pig : _____
7. goat : cow *as* kid : _____

C. MATCHING: ASSOCIATIONS

_e_ 1. chicken   a. milk
___ 2. cow   b. fruit
___ 3. orchard   c. help
___ 4. irrigation system d. animals
___ 5. hired hand   e. eggs
___ 6. scarecrow   f. water
___ 7. barn   g. morning
___ 8. rooster   h. birds

D. MATCHING

_b_ 1. pig   a. house
___ 2. chicken   b. sty
___ 3. hen   c. tree
___ 4. fruit   d. coop
___ 5. vegetable e. system
___ 6. irrigation f. garden

113

A. WHICH WORD?

1. We gave her a (slug (kitten)) for her birthday.
2. Different types of zebras have different types of (horns   stripes).
3. It's time to feed the (worm   gerbil).
4. This sweater is made from the wool of the (llama   rhinoceros).
5. Do you want to ride the (hyena   pony)?
6. Look at the (bison   squirrel) in that tree!
7. Let's go see the (monkeys   rats) at the zoo.
8. Every morning I take my (puppy   chipmunk) for a walk.

B. MATCHING: *WHICH ANIMAL IS IT?*

_e_ **1.** beaver   **a.** It *throws* its quills.
___ **2.** skunk   **b.** Its odour is unpleasant.
___ **3.** hyena   **c.** It sleeps upside down.
___ **4.** bat   **d.** Its kids are in its pouch.
___ **5.** porcupine   **e.** Its teeth are very strong.
___ **6.** kangaroo   **f.** Its laugh is like a human's.

___ **7.** anteater   **g.** It's from Australia.
___ **8.** polar bear   **h.** It uses its hands like a human.
___ **9.** koala   **i.** It's from China.
___ **10.** chimpanzee   **j.** It lives in the ground.
___ **11.** worm   **k.** It lives at the North Pole.
___ **12.** panda   **l.** It eats insects.

C. ANALOGIES

dog	quills	wolf	foal	gibbon
rhinoceros	mouse	lion	beaver	zebra

1. fawn : deer *as* ____foal____ : horse
2. elephant : tusk *as* _____ : horn
3. wolf : wolves *as* _____ : mice
4. leopard : spots *as* _____ : stripes
5. horse : tail *as* _____ : mane
6. camel : desert *as* _____ : river
7. cat : kitten *as* _____ : puppy
8. whiskers : cat *as* _____ : porcupine
9. mouse : hamster *as* _____ : baboon
10. cat : mouse *as* _____ : rabbit

D. WHICH WORD DOESN'T BELONG?

1. horse	foal	(raccoon)	pony
2. mice	wolves	rats	guinea pigs
3. antler	buffalo	tusk	horn
4. pouch	quill	whiskers	tail
5. panda	koala	gorilla	grizzly bear
6. kitten	puppy	foal	mouse
7. hamster	armadillo	dog	gerbil

E. MATCHING: *WHAT DO THEY EAT?*

_b_ **1.** mice   **a.** leaves of tall trees
___ **2.** squirrels   **b.** cheese
___ **3.** bats   **c.** grass and bark
___ **4.** deer   **d.** fish
___ **5.** horses   **e.** insects
___ **6.** giraffes   **f.** nuts and seeds
___ **7.** polar bears   **g.** soil
___ **8.** worms   **h.** hay

F. LISTENING: *WHAT ANIMAL IS IT?*

Listen and circle the correct word.

1. rat	(bat)		**6.** foal	fawn
2. mouse	moose		**7.** monkey	donkey
3. bison	lion		**8.** anteater	beaver
4. raccoon	kangaroo		**9.** polar bear	koala bear
5. hyena	zebra		**10.** leopard	gopher

G. MAKING COMPARISONS

pig	owl	fox	cow	bear	bat	beaver	mouse	bull	donkey

1. as hungry as a _____ _bear_ _____   **6.** as big as a _____
2. as sly as a _____   **7.** as quiet as a _____
3. as stubborn as a _____   **8.** as wise as an _____
4. as fat as a _____   **9.** as blind as a _____
5. as strong as a _____   **10.** as busy as a _____

H. LISTENING: *WHICH ANIMAL IS IT?*

Listen and circle the correct word.

1. (porcupine) squirrel		**3.** camel	bison		**5.** zebra	leopard
2. armadillo moose		**4.** rhinoceros	elephant		**6.** hamster	lion

A. WHICH BIRD?

Look at page 118 of the Picture Dictionary and circle the correct word.

1. A bird with excellent eyesight that comes out at night is the ((owl) sparrow).
2. The smallest bird is the (pheasant hummingbird).
3. A bird that usually lives in the city is the (pigeon hawk).
4. A bird that can learn to speak is the (ostrich parrot).
5. A bird that doesn't fly is the (cardinal penguin).
6. The bird with feathers that look like many *eyes* is the (woodpecker peacock).
7. The bird that is the symbol of the United States is the (crow eagle).

B. WHICH INSECT?

Look at page 118 of the Picture Dictionary and circle the correct word.

1. The insect with eight legs is the (ant (spider)).
2. The insect that shines a light at night is the (firefly wasp).
3. The insect that makes dogs scratch is the (beetle flea).
4. The insect that becomes a butterfly is the (centipede caterpillar).
5. The insect that eats wood is the (termite ladybug).
6. The insect that drinks blood is the (moth tick).
7. The insect that makes honey is the (butterfly bee).
8. The insect that *sings* in the evenings is the (lightning bug cricket).

C. ANALOGIES

| feather | woodpecker | web | bill | cockroach | nest |

1. beehive : bee *as* _____nest_____ : robin
2. beak : woodpecker *as* _____ : duck
3. firefly : lightning bug *as* _____ : roach
4. nest : bird *as* _____ : spider
5. hummingbird : flower *as* _____ : wood
6. wing : butterfly *as* _____ : peacock

D. LISTENING: *WHICH BIRD OR INSECT?*

Listen and circle the correct answer.

1. (woodpecker) bee   4. wasp   spider
2. eagle   swan   5. cockatoo   caterpillar
3. beetle   duck   6. scorpion   pelican

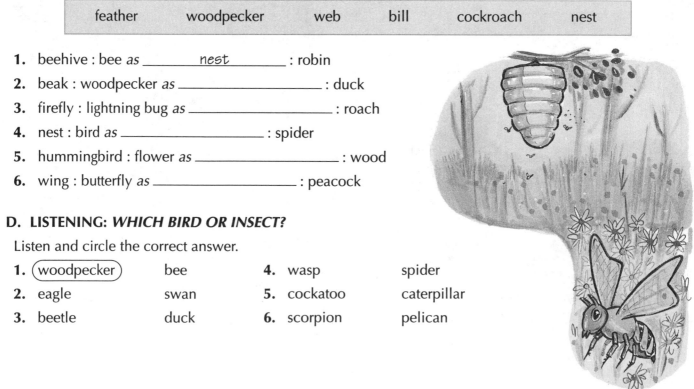

A. MATCHING: *ASSOCIATIONS*

b **1.** eel
___ **2.** octopus
___ **3.** turtle
___ **4.** tadpole
___ **5.** shark
___ **6.** dolphin

a. swimmer's enemy
b. electric
c. eight
d. friendly
e. slow-moving
f. baby frog

B. ANALOGIES

| claw | seal | snake | starfish | mussels | alligator | lizard |

1. fish : bass *as* _____snake_____ : cobra
2. salmon : fish *as* _____ : reptile
3. turtle : tortoise *as* _____ : crocodile
4. tentacle : octopus *as* _____ : lobster
5. trout : salmon *as* _____ : oysters
6. octopus : eight *as* _____ : five
7. fish : tail *as* _____ : flipper

C. WHICH WORD DOESN'T BELONG?

1. (seal)   tail   gill   fin
2. rattlesnake   walrus   cobra   boa constrictor
3. clam   mussel   scallop   whale
4. flounder   lobster   squid   shrimp
5. lobster   eel   shrimp   crab
6. crab   seal   walrus   otter
7. jellyfish   snail   iguana   squid
8. tadpole   tusk   claw   shell

D. JOURNAL ENTRY

Which fish, sea animals, and reptiles do people commonly eat in your country? How do they prepare them? Which ones do you like? Which ones don't you like? Why?

....
....
....
....
....
....

A. WHICH HAS THE SAME MEANING?

_b_ **1.** How wide is it?
____ **2.** How tall is it?
____ **3.** How deep is it?
____ **4.** How long is it?
____ **5.** How far is it?

a. What's the distance?
b. What's the width?
c. What's the length?
d. What's the height?
e. What's the depth?

B. ANALOGIES

square	wide	ellipse	diameter	triangle	metre	depth

1. length : long *as* _____depth_____ : deep
2. foot : mile *as* _____ : kilometre
3. circle : cone *as* _____ : pyramid
4. square : four *as* _____ : three
5. rectangle: square *as* _____ : circle
6. diagonal : rectangle *as* _____ : circle
7. high: height *as* _____ : width

C. MATCHING: *ABBREVIATIONS*

_c_ **1.** centimetre
____ **2.** foot
____ **3.** yard
____ **4.** mile
____ **5.** inch
____ **6.** kilometre
____ **7.** metre

a. yd.
b. mi.
c. cm
d. "
e. km
f. m
g. '

D. WHAT DOES IT EQUAL?

foot	mile	inch	yard

1. 1.6 km   1 ___mile___

2. 2.54 cm   1 _____

3. 0.914 m   1 _____

4. 0.305 m   1 _____

A. DO YOU REMEMBER?

Canadian schoolchildren sometimes memorize the names of the nine planets by learning:

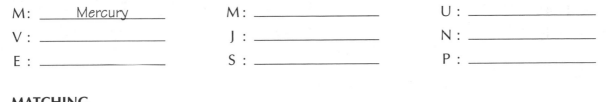

"My Very Energetic Mother Just Served Us Nine Pizzas."

Without looking in the Picture Dictionary, can you write the names of the nine planets in the correct order?

M : _____Mercury_____   M : _____   U : _____

V : _____   J : _____   N : _____

E : _____   S : _____   P : _____

B. MATCHING

_d_ **1.** lunar   **a.** pad

___ **2.** space   **b.** control

___ **3.** launch   **c.** shuttle

___ **4.** booster   **d.** eclipse

___ **5.** mission   **e.** rocket

C. CROSSWORD: *PICTURES TO WORDS*

ACROSS

2.   5.

7.   8.

9.

DOWN

1.   3.

4.   6.

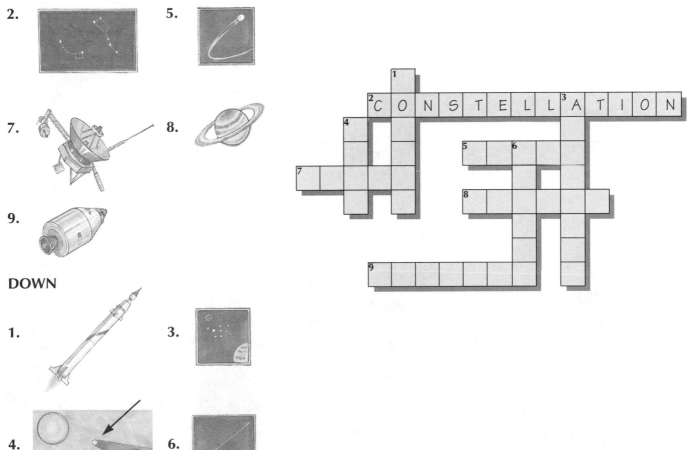

WORKBOOK PAGE 1

A. WHAT'S THE WORD?
1. first
2. family
3. phone
4. social insurance
5. apartment
6. postal
7. area

B. WHAT'S THE ANSWER?
1. d
2. c
3. a
4. b
5. h
6. e
7. g
8. f

WORKBOOK PAGE 2

A. WHICH GROUP?
wife	husband
mother	father
daughter	son
sister	brother
niece	nephew

B. HIS NAME OR HER NAME?
1. Her
2. His
3. Her
4. His
5. His
6. Her

C. WHO IS WHO?
1. e
2. f
3. d
4. a
5. c
6. b

D. IN OTHER WORDS
1. mother
2. father
3. grandfather
4. grandmother

WORKBOOK PAGES 3-4

A. WHICH GROUP?
aunt	cousin	uncle
niece		nephew
mother-in-law		father-in-law
daughter-in-law		son-in-law
sister-in-law		brother-in-law

B. WHICH WORD?
1. aunt, her
2. He's, he
3. His, nephew
4. niece, Her
5. uncle, cousin
6. she, husband

C. WHAT'S THE WORD?
1. sister
2. father
3. mother
4. brother
5. son
6. daughter

D. AT PAT AND JIM'S WEDDING
1. wife
2. sister
3. husband
4. parents
5. father
6. mother
7. nephew
8. son
9. sister
10. niece
11. brother

WORKBOOK PAGE 5

A. USING A COMPASS
	north
northwest	northeast
west	east
southwest	southeast
	south

B. USING THE MAP: *CANADA*
1. c
2. d
3. a
4. e
5. b

C. WHICH REGION?
1. British Columbia, Alberta, Saskatchewan, Manitoba
2. Labrador and Newfoundland (one province), Nova Scotia, Prince Edward Island, New Brunswick
3. Ontario, Quebec

WORKBOOK PAGE 6

A. WHICH CONTINENT
South America:	Europe:	Asia:	Africa:
Argentina	Austria	China	Egypt
Brazil	Germany	Japan	Nigeria
Chile	France	Korea	Zaire

B. A TRIP AROUND THE WORLD
1. Atlantic
2. Mediterranean
3. Indian
4. Pacific
5. Arctic

WORKBOOK PAGE 7

A. WHAT DO THEY DO?
1. get
2. takes
3. shaves
4. combs
5. get
6. have
7. brushes
8. washes
9. puts on
10. makes
11. say
12. go

B. CROSSWORD: *PICTURES AND WORDS (see p. 145)*

C. CROSSWORD: *WHAT DO WE DO? (see p. 145)*

D. WHAT'S THE SEQUENCE?
5
1
3
4
2
6

E. MATCHING
1. f
2. d
3. b
4. e
5. c
6. a

WORKBOOK PAGE 8

A. WHICH WORD?
1. floor
2. dishes
3. piano
4. play
5. iron
6. dog
7. floor
8. radio
9. TV
10. house

B. MATCHING
1. d
2. b
3. c
4. a
5. f
6. e

C. WHAT'S THE ACTION?
listen to	do	iron	watch
	feed	read	play

D. LISTENING: *WHAT ARE THEY DOING?*
Listen and choose the correct answer.

1. A. Tom, what are you doing?
   B. I'm feeding the baby.
2. A. Sally, what are you doing?
   B. I'm washing the dishes.
3. A. Michael, what are you doing?
   B. I'm playing the guitar.
4. A. Maria, what are you doing?
   B. I'm studying.
5. A. Bob, what are you doing?
   B. I'm ironing.
6. A. Janet, what are you doing?
   B. I'm watching TV.

Answers

1.	b	4.	a
2.	a	5.	a
3.	b	6.	b

WORKBOOK PAGE 9

A. WHERE ARE THE THINGS?
1. globe
2. overhead
3. clock
4. eraser
5. calculator
6. ruler

B. MATCHING
1. f
2. e
3. a
4. b
5. c
6. d

C. MATCHING: *COMPOUND WORDS*
1. textbook
2. loudspeaker
3. thumbtack
4. bookshelf

D. HOW DO WE USE THEM?
1. chalk
2. a pencil
3. a bookshelf
4. a thumbtack
5. a ruler
6. a calculator

WORKBOOK PAGE 10

A. THE TEACHER'S INSTRUCTIONS
1. hand
2. mistake
3. homework
4. test
5. papers
6. the shade
7. the answer
8. question
9. groups
10. the light

B. WHAT'S THE SEQUENCE?
5
2
4
6
1
3

C. WHAT ARE THEY DOING?
1. She's writing her name.
2. She's raising her hand.
3. He's putting away his book.
4. He's handing in his homework.
5. They're watching the movie.
6. He's taking out a piece of paper.

WORKBOOK PAGE 11

A. LANGUAGES AND COUNTRIES
1. England, the United States, Australia, New Zealand, Canada
2. Argentina, Bolivia, Chile, Colombia, the Dominican Republic, Ecuador, etc.
3. Egypt, Jordan, Saudi Arabia
4. Portugal, Brazil

B. COUNTRY, NATIONALITY, OR LANGUAGE?
1. Arabic
2. Argentina
3. France
4. Taiwanese
5. Poland
6. Vietnamese
7. Honduras
8. Jordanian
9. Romanian
10. Japanese

C. WHAT'S THE WORD?
1. Italian
2. Portuguese
3. Poland
4. Turkish
5. Latvian
6. Korean
7. Spanish
8. English

WORKBOOK PAGE 12

A. MATCHING
1. f
2. c
3. a
4. e
5. d
6. b

B. LISTENING: *CALLING FOR A TAXI*
Listen to the conversation. Write the number next to the correct words.

1. A. City Taxi Company.
   B. Hello. Please send a taxi to 23 Elm Street.
   A. Is that a house or an apartment?
   B. It's a single-family house.
2. A. Hello. This is Yellow Taxi.
   B. Hello. Please send a taxi to 511 45th Street.
   A. Is that a house or apartment?
   B. It's a townhouse.
3. A. Good morning. This is Red Top Taxi.
   B. Good morning. Could you send a taxi to 3210 M Street?
   A. Okay. Is that a private home?
   B. No. It's a residence.
4. A. Diamond Taxi.
   B. Hello. We need a taxi at 34 Rose Court.
   A. Is there an apartment number?
   B. No. It's a mobile home.
5. A. Hello. Orange Cab. Can I help you?
   B. Yes. Please send a taxi to 4520 Lee Highway.
   A. Is that a house or an apartment?
   B. It's a nursing home.

Answers

3	2	4	5	1

C. CROSSWORD *(see p. 145)*

WORKBOOK PAGE 13

A. MAKING LISTS

List 3 things you can sit on:	*List 4 things you can plug in:*	
armchair	lamp	VCR
soft/couch	television	stereo system
loveseat		

B. WHERE IS IT?
1. television
2. lamp
3. drapes
4. photograph
5. pillow
6. plant
7. speaker

C. ANALOGIES
1. floor
2. fireplace
3. end table
4. wall unit
5. couch
6. video cassette recorder

WORKBOOK PAGE 14

A. MAKING LISTS

List 6 things on the table:	*List 4 things on the buffet:*	*List 4 things on the serving cart:*
candlestick	salad bowl	teapot
tablecloth	pitcher	coffee pot
centrepiece	serving bowl	creamer
salt shaker	serving platter	sugar bowl
pepper shaker		
butter dish		

B. MATCHING

1.	f	4.	c
2.	a	5.	d
3.	e	6.	b

C. MATCHING: *COMPOUND WORDS*

1.	teapot	3.	centrepiece
2.	tablecloth	4.	candlestick

D. WHICH WORD DOESN'T BELONG?

1. candle (The others hold liquids.)
2. sugar bowl (The others are furniture.)
3. chandelier (The others go on a table.)
4. tablecloth (The others hold food or liquid.)
5. serving bowl (The others are furniture.)
6. table (The others are for light.)

E. LISTENING: *WHAT DO THEY NEED?*

Listen to the conversation. Write the number next to the correct words.

1. A. Would you like a glass of water?
   B. Yes, thank you.
2. A. Would you like a cup of tea?
   B. Yes, thank you.
3. A. Would you care for a cup of coffee?
   B. Yes, thank you.
4. A. Could you pass the butter, please?
   B. Yes, of course.
5. A. Would you like sugar in your tea?
   B. Yes, please.

Answers

2   3   1   4   5

WORKBOOK PAGE 15

A. ON THE TABLE

1.	wine glass	5.	butter knife
2.	teaspoon	6.	dinner fork
3.	knife	7.	tablecloth
4.	napkin	8.	soup spoon

B. WHICH WORD?

1.	fork	4.	glass
2.	bowl	5.	saucers
3.	knife	6.	napkin

WORKBOOK PAGE 16

A. THINGS FOR THE BEDROOM

1.	headboard	5.	mirror
2.	pillowcase	6.	jewelry box
3.	electric	7.	clock radio
4.	alarm clock	8.	blinds

B. WHICH WORD DOESN'T BELONG?

1. cot (The others are bed coverings.)
2. blinds (The others are parts of a bed.)
3. clock radio (The others are bed coverings.)
4. mirror (The others are types of beds.)
5. king-size bed (The others are smaller beds.)
6. mirror (The others are bed coverings.)
7. jewelry box (The others are bed coverings.)

C. MAKE THE BED!

4
5
1
6
3
2

D. LISTENING: *WHAT IS IT?*

Listen to the conversation about beds. Write the number under the correct picture.

1. A. Excuse me. I'm looking for a trundle bed.
   B. We have some very nice trundle beds on sale this week.
2. A. Excuse me. Do you have any bunk beds?
   B. Yes. We have bunk beds right over here.
3. A. I'm looking for a sofa bed.
   B. What kind of sofa bed are you interested in?
4. A. Excuse me. We need a cot. Do you sell cots at this store?
   B. Yes, we do. Come right over here.
5. A. Do you have any twin beds on sale this week?
   B. Yes, we do.

Answers

3   2   5   4   1

WORKBOOK PAGE 17

A. WHERE ARE THEY?

1.	placemats	5.	toaster
2.	cutting board	6.	microwave (oven)
3.	refrigerator magnet	7.	cookbook
4.	paper towel holder	8.	(electric) can opener

B. MATCHING

1.	c	5.	f
2.	d	6.	b
3.	g	7.	e
4.	a		

C. MATCHING: *COMPOUND WORDS*

1.	cookbook	3.	placemat
2.	potholder	4.	dishwasher

D. CROSSWORD (see p. 146)

WORKBOOK PAGE 18

A. MAKING A LIST

pressure cooker	toaster oven	electric frying pan
coffeemaker	electric mixer	waffle iron
coffee grinder	food processor	electric griddle
popcorn maker	blender	

B. WHAT'S THE WORD?

1.	coffee grinder	4.	can opener
2.	popcorn maker	5.	egg beater
3.	bottle opener	6.	vegetable peeler

C. WHICH WORD?

1.	food processor	4.	colander
2.	garlic press	5.	bottle opener
3.	kettle		

D. MATCHING: *ASSOCIATIONS*

1.	d	4.	e
2.	a	5.	c
3.	b		

WORKBOOK PAGE 19

A. MATCHING: *ASSOCIATIONS*

1.	b	4.	e
2.	d	5.	a
3.	c		

B. WHICH WORD?

1. cradle
2. doll
3. high chair
4. rattle
5. portable crib
6. diaper pail
7. toy chest
8. baby carrier

C. WHICH WORD DOESN'T BELONG?

1. mobile (The others move a baby around)
2. crib (The others are toys.)
3. diaper pail (The others are furniture a baby can sit in.)
4. stretch suit (The others are items a baby can sit in.)
5. toy chest (The others are toys.)
6. intercom (The others are items a baby sits on.)

D. MATCHING

1. c
2. j
3. h
4. a
5. i
6. d
7. e
8. b
9. f
10. g

WORKBOOK PAGE 20

A. WHICH WORD?

1. shampoo
2. vitamins
3. teething ring
4. soother
5. formula
6. disposable
7. cotton swabs
8. bib
9. teething ring
10. nipple

B. LISTENING: *WHAT ARE THEY TALKING ABOUT?*
Listen to the conversation. Circle the correct words.

1. A. Excuse me. I can't find the liquid vitamins.
   B. We're out of liquid vitamins. We'll have them tomorrow.
2. A. Where did you put the teething ring?
   B. It's in the playpen.
3. A. I can't find the baby wipes. Where did you put them?
   B. The baby wipes are next to the changing table.
4. A. Where are disposable diapers? I can't find them.
   B. Disposable diapers are in the next aisle.
5. A. Excuse me. Where is baby formula?
   B. Sorry. We're out of formula, but we'll have more tomorrow.
6. A. Honey? Where did you put the soother?
   B. I think it's in the crib.

Answers

1. liquid vitamins
2. teething ring
3. baby wipes
4. disposable diapers
5. formula
6. soother

C. CROSSWORD (see p. 146)

WORKBOOK PAGE 21

A. WHERE ARE THEY?

1. hamper
2. shelf
3. curtain
4. mirror
5. toothbrush
6. plunger
7. cup

B. MATCHING

1. e
2. d
3. a
4. c
5. b
6. i
7. h
8. j
9. f
10. g

C. WHICH WORD?

1. sponge
2. hamper
3. soap
4. rack
5. toilet
6. fan
7. shower curtain
8. seat
9. scale
10. shower

D. THINGS IN THE BATHROOM

1. fan
2. cup
3. soap
4. shelf
5. drain
6. sink

WORKBOOK PAGE 22

A. MATCHING: *ASSOCIATIONS*

1. c
2. a
3. f
4. b
5. d
6. e

B. MATCHING: *HOW DO WE USE THEM?*

1. c
2. a
3. b
4. f
5. d
6. e

C. WHICH WORD DOESN'T BELONG?

1. mascara (The others are used for their scents.)
2. shower cap (The others are liquid hair care products.)
3. nail polish (The others are used in the hair.)
4. hairspray (The others are dental hygiene products.)
5. tweezers (The others are makeup.)
6. shoe polish (The others involve care of the fingernails.)

D. LISTENING: *WHAT ARE THEY TALKING ABOUT?*
Listen to the commercials. What products are they describing? Check the correct answers.

1. Use it every day after you brush your teeth, and your teeth will be clean and healthy!
2. Your face will feel smooth all day!
3. Use it on shoes, boots, even pocketbooks! For a shine that lasts and lasts!
4. Keeps hair clean and shiny...smells nice, too!
5. Leaves lips shiny and moist...protects lips from the sun, too!
6. For that clean smell in every room of the house!
7. Put just a little blush on your cheeks for that healthy look!
8. Use the makeup base that looks perfect on you!
9. You'll smell fresh and clean all day!

Answers

1. dental floss
2. electric razor
3. shoe polish
4. shampoo
5. lipstick
6. air freshener
7. blush
8. foundation
9. deodorant

WORKBOOK PAGE 23

A. WHAT ARE THEY?

1. hanger
2. dustpan
3. recycling
4. iron
5. dryer
6. bleach
7. sponge
8. clothespins

B. WHICH WORD?

1. vacuum
2. sponge mop
3. fabric softener
4. dryer
5. clothesline
6. bleach
7. hanger
8. garbage can

C. MATCHING

1. d
2. e
3. a
4. h
5. b
6. g
7. f
8. c

D. WHICH WORD DOESN'T BELONG?

1. hanger (The others are used for cleaning.)
2. sponge (The others hold things.)
3. starch (The others are appliances.)
4. floor wax (The others are containers.)
5. iron (The others are laundry powders or liquids.)
6. laundry bag (The others are used for cleaning.)

WORKBOOK PAGE 24

A. HOME REPAIRS

1. roof
2. antenna
3. satellite
4. lamppost
5. back
6. doorknob
7. screens
8. lawnmower
9. lawn chair
10. patio

B. MATCHING: *ASSOCIATIONS*

1. c
2. d
3. a
4. b
5. h
6. g
7. e
8. f

C. CROSSWORD (see p. 147)

WORKBOOK PAGE 25

A. MY APARTMENT BUILDING

1. doorman
2. intercom
3. mailboxes
4. elevator
5. chute
6. laundry
7. room
8. lot
9. swimming pool
10. lock
11. peephole
12. detector

B. MATCHING: *COMPOUND WORDS*

1. peephole
2. doorman
3. mailbox
4. whirlpool

C. WHICH WORD?

1. doorbell
2. buzzer
3. lot
4. fire alarm
5. garbage chute
6. storage room
7. air conditioner
8. peephole

WORKBOOK PAGES 26-27

A. REPAIR AND SERVICE PEOPLE

1. locksmith
2. plumber
3. gardener
4. carpenter
5. exterminator
6. painter

B. HELP!

1. exterminator
2. plumber
3. appliance repair person
4. electrician
5. gardener
6. chimney sweep
7. painter
8. handyman

C. MATCHING

1. e
2. b
3. a
4. f
5. d
6. c

D. WHAT KIND OF BILLS ARE THESE?

1. telephone bill
2. water bill
3. cable TV bill
4. electric bill
5. pest control bill
6. mortgage payment
7. gas bill
8. oil/heating bill

WORKBOOK PAGE 28

A. HOW ARE THEY USED?

...cut.	...paint.	...fasten things together.
hacksaw	paint pan	hammer
hatchet	paint roller	screwdriver
saw	paintbrush/brush	wrench
power saw	paint	pliers
	nail	

B. WHICH TOOLS?

1. hammer
2. bit
3. paint thinner
4. sandpaper
5. hatchet
6. paint
7. power saw
8. pliers

C. WHICH WORD DOESN'T BELONG?

1. toolbox (The others are tools.)
2. saw (The others are used for fastening.)
3. pliers (The others are used for painting.)
4. screw (The others are used for cutting.)
5. sandpaper (The others are tools.)
6. wire (The others are tools.)

D. LISTENING: *WHAT ARE THEY TALKING ABOUT?*
Listen to the conversation. Circle the correct word.

1. A. Could I borrow your hand drill?
   B. Sure.
2. A. Where's the screwdriver?
   B. It's over there.
3. A. Where's the paint thinner?
   B. It's over there.
4. A. Where's the bit?
   B. It's over there
5. A. Where's the vise?
   B. It's over there.
6. A. Could I borrow your brace?
   B. Sure.
7. A. I need a washer.
   B. Look over there.
8. A. Could I please borrow your level?
   B. Of course.
9. A. Could I please borrow your hatchet?
   B. Sure. No problem.

Answers

1. hand drill
2. screwdriver
3. paint thinner
4. bit
5. vise
6. brace
7. washer
8. level
9. hatchet

WORKBOOK PAGE 29

A. WHICH WORD?

1. mousetrap
2. plunger
3. sidewalk salt
4. glue
5. vegetable seeds
6. flashlight
7. an extension cord
8. lawnmower
9. snow shovel
10. fly swatter

B. MATCHING: *SENTENCES*

1. c
2. d
3. h
4. b
5. a
6. g
7. e
8. f

C. MATCHING

1. e
2. d
3. b
4. a
5. c
6. h
7. j
8. f
9. g
10. i

D. LISTENING: *WHAT ARE THEY TALKING ABOUT?*
Listen to the conversation. Circle the correct word.

1. A. Where are the work gloves?
   B. I lent them to the neighbours.
2. A. I can't find the trowel.
   B. I put the trowel in the tool shed.
3. A. Where's the plunger?
   B. In the bathroom.
4. A. I think we blew a fuse.
   B. I'll check it out.
5. A. Where did you put the step ladder?
   B. I don't remember!
6. A. We need oil.
   B. Okay. I'll get some at the hardware store.

7. A. Please get some fertilizer at the store.
   B. Okay. I'll get the kind that sprays from the hose.
8. A. We need insect spray.
   B. You're right. All these bugs are making me sick!
9. A. Can you help me move this wheelbarrow?
   B. Sure. I'll put it in the toolshed.

Answers

1. gloves	4. fuse	7. fertilizer
2. trowel	5. step ladder	8. insect spray
3. plunger	6. oil	9. wheelbarrow

WORKBOOK PAGE 30

A. MATCHING: *CARDINAL AND ORDINAL NUMBERS*

1. c	5. a
2. g	6. b
3. d	7. h
4. f	8. e

B. WHICH NUMBER?

1. fifteen	5. twentieth
2. ninth	6. twenty-first
3. third	7. fifty
4. ten	8. first

C. CROSSWORD: *NUMBERS TO WORDS* (see p. 147)

D. LISTENING: *WHAT'S THE NUMBER?*
Circle the correct number.
1. My youngest son is nine years old.
2. This is the fifth time I've been here.
3. We've been married for fourteen years.
4. My best friend lives on the eleventh floor of that apartment building.
5. There are eleven students in the class.
6. I bought this on sale for thirty-two dollars!
7. My uncle is fifty-five years old.
8. They're celebrating their thirteenth wedding anniversary.

Answers

1. nine	5. 11
2. fifth	6. 32
3. 14	7. 55
4. 11th	8. 13th

WORKBOOK PAGES 31-32

A. MATCHING: WORDS

1. c	3. d
2. a	4. b

B. MATCHING: *NUMBERS AND WORDS*

1. d	5. f
2. c	6. h
3. a	7. e
4. b	8. g

C. MATH SENTENCES

1. $3 \times 6 = 18$	3. $6 + 12 = 18$
2. $20 - 6 = 14$	4. $20 \div 2 = 10$

D. MATCHING: *WORDS AND FRACTIONS*

1. c	4. b
2. e	5. d
3. a	

E. WHAT FRACTION IS IT?
3/4   1/2   2/3   1/4   1/3

F. LISTENING: *WHAT'S THE FRACTION?*
Listen and write the number under the correct fraction.
1. One third of the class is absent today.
2. We'll leave in three quarters of an hour.
3. One fourth of the students in the class are from Europe.
4. The bicycle costs half the regular price.
5. The gas tank is about two thirds full.

Answers

4	2	5	1	3

G. MATCHING: *WORDS AND PERCENTS*

1. c	4. b
2. e	5. f
3. a	6. d

H. WHAT PERCENT IS IT?
100%   50%   75%   25%   66 2/3%

I. LISTENING: WHAT'S THE PERCENT?
Listen and write the number under the correct percent.
1. She got one hundred percent on the English test.
2. There's a sixty percent chance of snow tonight.
3. Twenty-five percent of the class has blue eyes.
4. The salesman took fifty percent off the regular price.
5. He got seventy-five percent of the answers right.

Answers

3	5	4	1	2

WORKBOOK PAGE 33

A. WHAT TIME IS IT?

1. 4:30	2. 4:00	3. 4:05
4. 4:15	5. 4:45	6. 4:40

B. MATCHING: *TIME*
1. 4:45, four forty-five
2. 5:30, five thirty
3. 5:40, twenty to six
4. 5:20, twenty after five
5. 5:50, ten to six

C. WHEN IS IT?

1. A.M.	3. midnight
2. noon	4. P.M.

D. LISTENING: *WHAT'S THE TIME?*
Listen and circle the correct time.
1. A. Excuse me. Could you tell me what time it is?
   B. Yes. It's three o'clock exactly.
2. A. What time will we arrive?
   B. At five ten a.m.
3. A. Excuse me. When does the train leave?
   B. At one oh five.
4. A. Excuse me. Do you have the time?
   B. Yes. It's five minutes after seven.
5. A. Excuse me. When will the train arrive?
   B. The train should arrive at about a quarter to four.
6. A. What time does the movie begin?
   B. At a quarter to eight.

Answers

1. 3:00	4. 7:05
2. 5:10	5. 3:45
3. 1:05	6. 7:45

WORKBOOK PAGE 34

B. USING THE CALENDAR

1. Thursday	4. Tuesday
2. Friday	5. Monday
3. Saturday	6. Wednesday

C. DATES: *WORDS TO NUMBERS*

1. 9/3/49	4. 2/12/95
2. 1/16/70	5. 11/10/76
3. 3/26/83	6. 12/12/12

D. DATES: *NUMBERS TO WORDS*

1. April 16, 1978	4. July 20, 1995
2. October 1, 1996	5. May 25, 1956
3. August 26, 1980	6. September 3, 1985

E. SEQUENCE

3	6	11	5
4	2	10	1
12	7	8	9

WORKBOOK PAGE 35

A. MAKING A LIST

bakery   coffee shop
cafeteria   convenience store
donut shop   delicatessen/deli
grocery store

B. WHICH PLACE?

1. barber shop
2. bakery
3. dry cleaners
4. pharmacy
5. furniture store
6. delicatessen
7. service station
8. donut shop
9. flower shop
10. concert hall

C. CROSSWORD: *PICTURES TO WORDS* (see p. 148)

WORKBOOK PAGE 36

A. GOING SHOPPING

1. mall
2. garage
3. music
4. pet
5. photo
6. toy
7. pizza
8. restaurant
9. theatre

B. ANALOGIES

1. vision centre
2. jewelry store
3. library
4. post office
5. travel agency
6. music store

C. MATCHING: *PLACES AND ACTIONS*

1. c
2. h
3. f
4. b
5. a
6. g
7. d
8. e

D. LISTENING: *WHERE ARE THEY?*

Listen to the conversation and circle the correct place.

1. A. Two tickets, please.
   B. For which movie?
   A. For "Home Alone 3."
2. A. We need a room for two nights.
   B. For how many people?
   A. For 2 adults and 2 children.
3. A. I'd like to look at engagement rings, please.
   B. Would you like to look at diamond rings?
   A. Yes, please.
4. A. We'd like to go to San Francisco.
   B. Do you want to fly first class?
   A. No. First class isn't necessary.
5. A. I'd like to try these shoes on.
   B. Fine. What size do you wear?
   A. I wear a 7 and a half.
6. A. I'd like to see a menu, please.
   B. Certainly. Would you like something to drink?
   A. Yes, please.
7. A. I'd like 2 slices of pizza, please.
   B. Is that to go or to eat here?
   A. I'll take it to go.
8. A. I'd like chocolate and vanilla, please.
   B. In a cone or a cup?
   A. In a cone.

Answers

1. movie theatre
2. motel
3. jewelry store
4. travel agency
5. shoe store
6. restaurant
7. pizza shop
8. ice cream shop

WORKBOOK PAGE 37

A. WHERE IS IT?

1. bus
2. street
3. sidewalk
4. manhole
5. courthouse
6. subway station
7. fire station
8. intersection

B. MATCHING: *ASSOCIATIONS*

1. d
2. c
3. b
4. e
5. f
6. a

C. IN THE CITY

1. crosswalk
2. street sign
3. public telephone
4. newsstand
5. restaurant
6. taxi
7. intersection
8. parking enforcement officer

WORKBOOK PAGES 38-39

A. WHAT'S THE ANSWER?

1. long	2. bad	3. tall
4. loose	5. hot	6. single
7. wide	8. wet	9. dirty

B. ANTONYMS

1. young
2. new
3. heavy
4. dark
5. sharp
6. shiny
7. tall
8. long
9. easy
10. soft
11. curly
12. crooked

C. MY CAR

1. new
2. old
3. neat
4. fast
5. quiet
6. fancy
7. pretty
8. small
9. good
10. inexperience

D. CROSSWORD: *OPPOSITES* (see p. 148)

WORKBOOK PAGE 40

A. WHICH COLUMN?

happy emotions:	*sad emotions:*
proud	annoyed
ecstatic	miserable
pleased	disappointed
	frustrated

B. WHICH WORD?

1. cold
2. surprised
3. thirsty
4. sick
5. exhausted

C. MATCHING: *ASSOCIATIONS*

1. e
2. d
3. b
4. c
5. a

D. ANALOGIES

1. ecstatic
2. sick
3. cold
4. tired
5. unhappy

WORKBOOK PAGE 41

A. WHICH FRUIT DOESN'T BELONG?

1. lime
2. coconut
3. apricot
4. pineapple
5. strawberry

B. LISTENING: *WHAT FRUIT ARE THEY TALKING ABOUT?*

Circle the correct word.

1. A. I'm hungry. Do we have any fruit?
   B. Yes. We have apples.
2. A. Would you like a plum?
   B. Yes. Plums are delicious!
3. A. Where did you get the papaya?
   B. At the supermarket.
4. A. Do we have any more grapes?
   B. No. I'll get some tomorrow.
5. A. Would you like some watermelon?
   B. Yes, thank you.
6. A. Do we have any nectarines?
   B. No. I'll get some at the supermarket.
7. A. These cranberries are delicious!
   B. I like them, too.
8. A. Would you like a coconut?
   B. Yes, thank you.

Answers

1. apples
2. plums
3. papayas
4. grapes
5. watermelon
6. nectarines
7. cranberries
8. coconut

C. CROSSWORD: *PICTURES TO WORDS* (see p. 149)

WORKBOOK PAGE 42

A. WHICH GROUP?

1. lima bean
2. zucchini
3. yam
4. scallion

B. MATCHING

1. b
2. e
3. a
4. c
5. d

C. CROSSWORD: *PICTURES TO WORDS* (see p. 149)

WORKBOOK PAGES 43-44

A. WHICH GROUP?

Packaged Goods:	Beverages:	Canned Goods:	Dairy Products:
rice	diet pop	canned	milk
cereal	pop	vegetables	cheese
noodles	bottled water	soup	eggs
		tuna fish	

B. WHICH WORD?

1. milk
2. cream
3. cheese
4. fish
5. juice
6. juice
7. packs
8. pop

C. MORE GROUPS

Meat:	Poultry:	Seafood:	Baked Goods:
beef	chicken	salmon	bread
roast	duck	flounder	cake
lamb	turkey	shellfish	rolls

D. WHERE ARE THEY?

1. Poultry
2. Meat
3. Seafood
4. Baked Goods
5. Frozen Foods

E. MATCHING: *WHERE ARE THESE FOODS?*

1. e
2. b
3. d
4. a
5. c
6. h
7. i
8. f
9. j
10. g

F. WHAT'S THE WORD?

1. wings
2. trout
3. lemonade
4. mussels
5. steak
6. rolls

G. LISTENING: *WHAT ARE THEY TALKING ABOUT?*

Circle the correct word.

1. A. Let's have steak tonight.
   B. Good idea!
2. A. Excuse me. I'm looking for duck.
   B. It's in the Poultry Section.
3. A. Let's have lamb for dinner tonight.
   B. That sounds good!
4. A. I'm going to the supermarket.
   B. Get some ribs for dinner tonight, okay?
5. A. Pardon me. Where can I find haddock?
   B. In the Seafood Section.
6. A. Are you going to the supermarket? We need a roast.
   B. Okay. I'll get it.
7. A. How about shellfish tonight?
   B. Okay. Let's have oysters.
8. A. Do we need chicken from the supermarket?
   B. Yes. Get some legs, please.

Answers

1. steak
2. duck
3. lamb
4. ribs
5. haddock
6. roast
7. oysters
8. legs

WORKBOOK PAGE 45

A. WHICH GROUP?

1. mozzarella
2. pretzels
3. cole slaw
4. cocoa
5. bologna
6. relish

B. MATCHING

1. c
2. e
3. d
4. f
5. b
6. a

C. MATCHING: *ASSOCIATIONS*

1. c
2. d
3. b
4. f
5. a
6. e

D. WHICH WORD?

1. basket
2. towels
3. diapers
4. aisle
5. bag
6. coupons

E. LISTENING: *WHAT SECTION?*
Listen to the conversation and circle the correct section.
1. A. Do we need any of these paper plates?
   B. No, but we need paper cups.
2. A. Paper or plastic bag?
   B. Paper, please. And here are my coupons.
3. A. This formula is on sale.
   B. Good. We can get some wipes, too.
4. A. We need coffee, don't we?
   B. No, but I'd like to get some herbal tea.
5. A. I think I'll bake a cake this weekend.
   B. Do you need this cake mix?
6. A. Let's pick up some turkey and bologna.
   B. Okay. The potato salad looks good, too.
7. A. Pick up some salt and pepper.
   B. We could use some salad dressing, too.
8. A. Let's buy some chips for the party tonight.
   B. Great. How about some pretzels, too?

Answers
1. Paper Products
2. Checkout Area
3. Baby Products
4. Coffee and Tea
5. Baking Products
6. Deli
7. Condiments
8. Snack Foods

WORKBOOK PAGE 46

A. WHAT'S THE CONTAINER?

box   roll   bag
bunch   can   jar

B. WHAT'S THE WORD?
1. kilogram
2. head
3. bar
4. litre
5. loaf
6. dozen
7. box
8. ear

C. WHICH WORD?
1. tub
2. packs
3. roll
4. litre
5. stick
6. head

D. LISTENING: *WHAT ARE THEY TALKING ABOUT?*
Listen to the conversation and circle the correct words.
1. A. What did you get at the supermarket?
   B. I got two six-packs of pop and a bag of chips.
2. A. Do you have more than eight items?
   B. No. I only have a loaf of bread.
3. A. Could you please pick up two litres of milk?
   B. Two litres? Certainly.
4. A. I bought a package of your favourite muffins.
   B. Thank you!
5. A. Would you pick up a bottle of ketchup at the supermarket?
   B. Sure. Is there anything else?
6. A. Would you like corn for dinner tonight?
   B. Yes. Let's get a few ears.
7. A. I'd like some ice cream for dessert tonight.
   B. Should I get a litre of vanilla or chocolate?
8. A. Let's get a couple of boxes of crackers for the party tonight.
   B. Okay. What kind do you like?

Answers
1. two six-packs
2. a loaf
3. two litres
4. package
5. bottle
6. a few ears
7. litre
8. boxes

WORKBOOK PAGE 47

A. MATCHING: *ABBREVIATIONS*
1. d
2. a
3. f
4. e
5. c
6. b

B. WHICH IS EQUAL?
1. d
2. c
3. a
4. b

C. WHICH WORD?
1. tablespoons
2. 250 g
3. cups
4. teaspoon
5. litre
6. cup

D. WHAT'S THE NUMBER?
1. 1
2. 2
3. 1
4. 4
5. 2
6. 2

E. LISTENING
Listen and circle the correct words.
1. A. How much flour should I put in?
   B. Add two cups.
2. A. These cookies are delicious! What did you put in them?
   B. A cup of nuts.
3. A. How much milk did you put in the scrambled eggs?
   B. One tablespoon.
4. A. How much ground beef would you like?
   B. I'd like half a kilogram, please.
5. A. These cookies are salty! How much salt did you put in?
   B. Two tablespoons.
6. A. I'd like 250 grams of turkey, please.
   B. Did you say 250 grams?
7. A. How much cheese should I put in?
   B. The recipe says 100 grams.
8. A. Could you pick up a litre of milk?
   B. A litre? Okay.

Answers
1. two cups
2. a cup
3. a tablespoon
4. half a kilogram
5. two tablespoons
6. 250 grams
7. 100 grams
8. litre

WORKBOOK PAGE 48

A. MATCHING
1. b
2. f
3. e
4. c
5. d
6. a

B. HELP IN THE KITCHEN
1. bake
2. beat
3. slice
4. pour
5. scrambling
6. stir-frying
7. barbecue
8. boil

C. SPELLING RULE
1. slicing
2. carving
3. scrambling
4. grating
5. baking
6. combining

WORKBOOK PAGE 49

A. ORDERING FAST FOOD
1. c
2. d
3. e
4. b
5. a

B. WHICH WORD DOESN'T BELONG?

1. taco (The others are beverages.)
2. BLT (The others are forms of bread.)
3. iced tea (The others are sandwiches.)
4. donut (The others are types of bread.)
5. chicken (The others are from beef.)
6. danish (The others are types of bread.)

C. LISTENING: *TAKING FAST FOOD ORDERS*

Listen to the order and put a check next to the correct item.

1. A. May I help you?
   B. Yes. I'll have a roast beef sandwich on white bread.
2. A. May I help you?
   B. Yes. I'll have a biscuit and a cup of coffee.
3. A. What would you like?
   B. I'd like a taco and a bowl of chili. Not too hot.
4. A. May I help you?
   B. Yes, thank you. Tuna fish on white.
5. A. Good afternoon. What can I get for you?
   B. Hello. I'll have a bacon, lettuce, and tomato sandwich. No mayonnaise.
6. A. May I help you?
   B. Yes. I'll have a chicken salad sandwich on rye.

Answers

1. roast beef	3. taco	5. BLT
2. biscuit	4. tuna fish	6. rye bread

WORKBOOK PAGES 50-51

A. ORDERING

1. shrimp cocktail
2. antipasto
3. veal cutlet
4. noodles
5. apple pie

B. LISTENING: *ORDERING AT A RESTAURANT*

You're a waiter or waitress. Listen to the order and check the correct items.

1. A. Good evening. May I take your order?
   B. Yes. For an appetizer I'll have the potato skins.
   A. And what kind of salad would you like?
   B. I'll have the spinach salad.
   A. And for the main course?
   B. I'd like the roast beef.
   A. What side dish would you like with that?
   B. I'll have the mixed vegetables.
   A. Would you care for dessert later?
   B. Yes. I think I'll have jello.
2. A. Hello. My name is John, and I'll be your waiter this evening. Are you ready to order?
   B. Yes. What do you recommend as an appetizer?
   A. The chicken wings are very good.
   B. Okay. I'll try them.
   A. What kind of salad do you care for today?
   B. Oh, just a tossed salad. No, wait a minute. I think I'll have a Greek salad.
   A. Okay. . . . And for an entree?
   B. How's the meatloaf?
   A. It's good. But the broiled fish is excellent.
   B. Okay I'll have the broiled fish. And can I have some rice with that?
   A. Certainly. And for dessert?
   B. I don't think I'll order dessert now. Maybe later.
   A. All right.

Answers

1. Appetizers: potato skins
   Salads: spinach salad
   Main Courses/Entrees: roast beef
   Side Dishes: mixed vegetables
   Desserts: jello

2. Appetizer: chicken wings
   Salads: Greek salad
   Main Courses/Entrees: broiled fish
   Side Dishes: rice
   Desserts: none

WORKBOOK PAGE 52

A. MATCHING: *ASSOCIATIONS*

1. c		4. f
2. a		5. d
3. e		6. b

B. WHICH COLOUR?

1. grey		4. red, white
2. blue		5. Gold
3. green		6. black, white

WORKBOOK PAGE 53

A. WHICH WORD?

1. shirt		4. jacket
2. gown		5. suit
3. sweater		6. skirt

B. MATCHING: *COMPOUND WORDS*

1. jumpsuit		3. overalls
2. turtleneck		4. necktie

C. MAKING CLOTHES

1. tie		5. vest
2. dress		6. gown
3. jeans		7. tights
4. coat		8. jacket

D. CROSSWORD: *PICTURES TO WORDS* (see p. 150)

WORKBOOK PAGE 54

A. WHICH WORD?

1. pyjamas		5. sandals
2. work boots		6. long underwear
3. sneakers		7. robe
4. slippers		

B. WHICH WORD DOESN'T BELONG?

1. underpants (The others are shoes.)
2. stockings (The others are types of shoes.)
3. boots (The others are underwear.)
4. pyjamas (The others are worn on the legs or feet.)
5. slip (The others are types of shoes.)
6. socks (The others are underwear.)

C. MATCHING

1. g		5. c
2. b		6. a
3. d		7. e
4. f		

D. LISTENING: *WHAT ARE THEY TALKING ABOUT?*

Listen to the conversation and circle the correct word.

1. A. I can't find my brand new shorts.
   B. Did you look for them in the dresser?
2. A. I bought some new high tops today.
   B. They look nice.
3. A. Have you seen my new slippers?
   B. They're probably in the closet.
4. A. I got some new pumps, but I can't find them.
   B. Did you look under the bed?
5. A. I need to get some new pyjamas.
   B. We can go shopping tonight.
6. A. Where are my new socks? Do you know?
   B. Hmm. Check in your bureau.

7. A. I'm looking for my nightshirt. Do you know where it is?
   B. Look in the wash.
8. A. New shoes?
   B. Yes. They are.
Answers
1. shorts
2. high tops
3. slippers
4. pumps
5. pyjamas
6. socks
7. nightshirt
8. shoes

WORKBOOK PAGE 55

A. WHICH GROUP?

jackets:	hats:	pants:
windbreaker	cap	tennis shorts
parka	beret	running shorts
down vest	rain hat	sweat pants

B. WHAT DO WE WEAR?

. . . when it's hot?	. . . when it's raining?	. . . when it's snowing?
tank top	rubbers	ear muffs
shorts	raincoat	ski jacket
sandals	poncho	mittens

C. MATCHING: *WHICH PART OF THE BODY?*
1. e
2. d
3. f
4. g
5. b
6. c
7. a

D. LISTENING: *WHAT ARE THEY TALKING ABOUT?*
Listen to the conversation and circle the correct word.
1. A. Is this hat yours?
   B. Yes. It's mine. Thanks.
2. A. What's the weather like?
   B. It's cool. Wear your overcoat.
3. A. I found these sweat pants.
   B. Thanks. They're mine.
4. A. I went shopping and got a new trenchcoat.
   B. Nice!
5. A. That's a nice beret you have on.
   B. Thank you.
6. A. It's cold outside today.
   B. Okay. I think I'll wear my parka.
7. A. It's going to be cold and snow all day today.
   B. I'll wear my ear muffs.
8. A. I found these tennis shorts in the dryer. Are they yours?
   B. Yes. They're mine. Thanks.
Answers
1. hat
2. overcoat
3. sweat pants
4. trenchcoat
5. beret
6. parka
7. ear muffs
8. tennis shorts

WORKBOOK PAGE 56

A. WHERE DO WE WEAR THEM?

neck:	finger:	wrist:	waist:
necklace	ring	bracelet	belt
beads	wedding band	watch	
chain			

B. MATCHING: *HOW DO WE USE THEM?*
1. d
2. e
3. b
4. h
5. a
6. g
7. f
8. c

C. MATCHING: *COMPOUND WORDS*
1. necklace
2. pocketbook
3. handbag
4. backpack
5. briefcase
6. earring

D. WHICH WORD DOESN'T BELONG?
1. wallet (The others are bags.)
2. key chain (The others are jewelry.)
3. key ring (The others are jewelry.)
4. bracelet (The others are bags.)
5. tote bag (The others are jewelry.)

WORKBOOK PAGE 57

A. WHAT'S THE WORD?
1. plain
2. low
3. wide
4. baggy
5. heavy
6. dark

B. WHAT'S THE WORD?
1. striped
2. narrow
3. baggy
4. long
5. light
6. small
7. narrow
8. long

C. LISTENING: *WHAT ARE THEY DESCRIBING?*
Listen to the conversation. Put the number next to the correct description.
1. How do you like this solid tie?
2. Are these plaid pants on sale?
3. I prefer the checked coat.
4. I really like that striped suit.
5. Your paisley scarf is so colourful!
6. I'm looking for a flowered skirt.
7. I prefer a simple print shirt.
8. How do you like the polka dot tie?
Answers

4	3	2	8
7	6	5	1

D. WHICH WORD DOESN'T BELONG?
1. tight
2. low
3. fancy
4. long
5. short
6. dark

WORKBOOK PAGE 58

A. MATCHING: *DEPARTMENTS*
1. e
2. a
3. b
4. c
5. g
6. d
7. h
8. f

B. WHICH WORD?
1. snack bar
2. directory
3. parking lot
4. customer pickup area
5. escalator
6. water fountain

C. LISTENING
Listen to the conversation. Write the number next to the correct place.
1. A. Excuse me. Are there any radios on sale?
   B. Yes, sir. They're over there, next to the tape recorders and clock radios.
2. A. What floor are you going to?
   B. The third floor. Could you push three for me, please?
3. A. I'll have a hot dog and a soda, please.
   B. Would you like a large or a small soda?
4. A. Try this. I think you'll like the smell.
   B. Hmm. "Sweet Scent". How much does a bottle of this cost?
5. A. My daughter usually wears a size 7 dress.
   B. Kids grow so fast. Maybe you should buy this dress in a size 8.
6. A. These earrings are lovely.
   B. Yes, they are. And we have a necklace that goes very well with them.

7. A. Which beds are on sale this week?
   B. The twin beds over there, next to the lamps.
8. A. Watch your step, Johnny. Put your hand on the railing.
   B. I like this better than the elevator, Mommy!
9. A. It's so hard to find a space!
   B. I see a man moving his car. Over there!

Answers

4	6
1	2
9	3
5	8
7	

WORKBOOK PAGE 59

A. ANOTHER WAY OF SAYING IT
1. compact disc
2. television
3. video cassette recorder
4. (personal) cassette player
5. video camera
6. sound system
7. boom box
8. cassette

B. MATCHING: *ASSOCIATIONS*
1. c
2. d
3. e
4. b
5. a

C. ANALOGIES
1. turntable
2. VCR
3. Walkman
4. audio cassette
5. videotape
6. headphones

D. MATCHING: *IDENTIFYING EQUIPMENT*
1. e
2. b
3. a
4. c
5. d

WORKBOOK PAGE 60

A. MATCHING: *WHAT EQUIPMENT DO YOU NEED?*
1. e
2. d
3. a
4. g
5. h
6. f
7. b
8. c

B. MATCHING
1. e
2. f
3. b
4. g
5. h
6. a
7. c
8. d

C. LISTENING: *USING A CHECKLIST*
Listen to the conversation. Check the equipment included.
1. A. I saw your ad in the newspaper. Is this the computer on sale?
   B. Yes, it is. It's on sale for one thousand one hundred dollars.
   A. Is the monitor included?
   B. Yes, it is.
   A. Is the disk drive included?
   B. Yes, it is. The monitor, the disk drive, the keyboard, and the mouse are all included.
   A. How about the printer?
   B. No, sir. The printer and modem are not included.
   A. And software?
   B. Software is extra, sir.
2. A. We're organizing our office and we need a reliable computer system.
   B. Yes, sir. Right over here is the best system we have. The complete system will cost two thousand five hundred dollars.
   A. And what does the system include?

B. This includes the basics: the monitor, the disk drive, the keyboard, and the mouse. It also includes the printer and a modem.
   A. And software?
   B. The computer system comes with data processing software.
3. A. Which camera is the best?
   B. This one here. It's on sale for 79 dollars.
   A. And what is included in the price?
   B. You get the camera, the camera case, the flash attachment, and one roll of film.

Answers

1.	2.	3.
✓ monitor	✓ monitor	✓ camera
✓ disk drive	✓ disk drive	__ zoom lens
✓ keyboard	✓ keyboard	✓ camera
✓ mouse	✓ mouse	case
__ printer	✓ printer	✓ flash
__ modem	✓ modem	attachment
__ software	✓ software	__ tripod
		✓ film

WORKBOOK PAGE 61

A. TOYS

Toys we use inside:	*Toys we use outside:*
train set	bicycle
video game system	pail and shovel
jigsaw puzzle	skateboard

B. MATCHING
1. e
2. a
3. b
4. c
5. d
6. i
7. h
8. f
9. j
10. g

C. WHAT'S THE WORD?
1. colouring book
2. rubber ball
3. tricycle
4. paint set
5. construction set
6. wading pool
7. doll house
8. stuffed animal

WORKBOOK PAGES 62-63

A. CANADIAN COINS
dime   loonie   nickel   quarter   two-dollar coin   penny

B. MATCHING
1. two dollars, two-dollar coin
2. five cents, nickel
3. ten cents, dime
4. one dollar, loonie
5. twenty-five cents, quarter
6. one cent, penny

C. AMOUNTS

5¢	25¢	6¢	35¢	50¢
$.05	$.25	$.06	$.35	$.50

D. CANADIAN CURRENCY
$10.00 $5.00 $25.00 $60.00 $120.00

E. MAKING CHANGE
1. $4.00
2. $.15 or 15¢
3. $5.00
4. $10.00
5. $.05 or 5¢
6. $100.00

F. LISTENING: *HOW MUCH?*
Listen to the conversation. Circle the correct amount.
1. A. Do you have enough money to go to the movies?
   B. Yes. I have ten dollars.
2. A. How much does it cost?
   B. Six fifty.
3. A. Do you have any change?
   B. I only have a dollar.

132

4. A. How much money do you have?
   B. I have five loonies and two quarters.
5. A. How much is it?
   B. Fifty-one dollars.
6. A. Do you have enough money?
   B. Yes. It only costs twenty-five dollars and thirty cents.
7. A. What's the cost?
   B. Fourteen fifty.
8. A. Do you have any cash?
   B. Let's see. . . I have twelve dollars and ten cents exactly.

Answers

1. $10.00
2. $6.50
3. $1.00
4. $5.50
5. $51.00
6. $25.30
7. $14.50
8. $12.10

WORKBOOK PAGES 64-65

A. IN THE BANK

1. teller
2. cheque
3. money order
4. chequebook
5. traveler's cheques
6. monthly statement
7. deposit slip
8. withdrawal slip

B. MATCHING

1. d
2. e
3. a
4. b
5. c
6. g
7. h
8. f

C. WHICH WORD DOESN'T BELONG?

1. automatic teller (The others are people.)
2. safe deposit box (The others are paper.)
3. ATM card (The others are paper.)
4. security guard (The others are printed items.)
5. loan application (The others relate to chequing.)

D. WHAT ARE YOU DOING?

1. 2945 5879
   Account Number

Total Withdrawal	$150.00

2. 1094 3875
   Account Number

Total Withdrawal	$250.00

3. 595 40985
   Account Number

TOTAL	$650.50

4. 4378 349
   Account Number

TOTAL	$450.30

5. (cheque for $115.00)
6. (cheque for 36.85)

WORKBOOK PAGES 66-67

A. WHICH WORD DOESN'T BELONG?

1. earlobe (The others are part of the leg.)
2. nose (The others are part of the eye.)
3. tongue (The others relate to hair.)
4. hip (The others are parts of the head.)
5. elbow (The others are part of the leg.)
6. armpit (The others relate to the mouth.)

B. MATCHING: *ASSOCIATIONS*

1. c
2. a
3. e
4. b
5. f
6. d

C. MATCHING: *CLOTHING AND THE BODY*

1. e
2. b
3. d
4. f
5. c
6. a

D. WHICH WORD?

1. beard
2. shin
3. hip
4. chin
5. forehead
6. leg
7. knee
8. tongue

E. WHICH WORD DOESN'T BELONG?

1. bones (The others are internal.)
2. veins (The others are parts of the hand.)
3. toenail (The others relate to fingers.)
4. skin (The others are parts of the foot.)
5. knuckle (The others relate to the circulation of blood.)
6. palm (The others are internal.)
7. muscle (The others are joints.)

F. MATCHING: *ASSOCIATIONS*

1. f
2. e
3. d
4. a
5. g
6. c
7. b

G. MATCHING: *CLOTHING AND THE BODY*

1. e
2. a
3. d
4. b
5. c

H. WHICH WORD?

1. lungs
2. fingernails
3. bones
4. heart
5. stomach
6. throat

I. LISTENING: *WHAT IS IT?*

Circle the correct word.

1. Oh! My stomach hurts!
2. I'm concerned about my tooth.
3. I'm glad to hear that your calf is okay.
4. My doctor wants me to have some tests for my bladder.
5. What's the matter with your skin?
6. My nose hurts!
7. My doctor is concerned about my hip.
8. I want to have some tests for my elbow.

Answers

1. stomach
2. tooth
3. calf
4. bladder
5. skin
6. nose
7. hip
8. elbow

WORKBOOK PAGES 68-69

A. MATCHING

1. i
2. f
3. a
4. c
5. b
6. h
7. e
8. g
9. j
10. d

B. WHAT'S THE MATTER?

1. stomachache
2. sunburn
3. stiff neck
4. chills
5. cavity
6. backache
7. diarrhea
8. virus
9. rash
10. sore throat

D. FEELING TERRIBLE

1. sprain
2. vomit
3. itchy
4. congested
5. dislocate
6. swollen
7. exhausted
8. burp
9. bleeding
10. coughing

E. CROSSWORD (see p. 150)

WORKBOOK PAGE 70

A. MATCHING: *WHAT DO THEY DO?*

1. h
2. e
3. a
4. g
5. i
6. d
7. b
8. j
9. c
10. f

B. WHAT WILL THEY USE?

1. Novocaine
2. thermometer
3. blood pressure gauge
4. X-ray machine
5. stethoscope
6. examination table
7. eye chart
8. scale

C. LISTENING: *WHO'S TALKING?*
Listen to the sentences. Circle the correct answer.

1. Your blood pressure is 90 over 60. That's good!
2. Your teeth are very clean now.
3. How do these glasses fit?
4. A good check-up! You don't have any cavities.
5. Congratulations! You're going to be a mother!
6. I'm going to look into your ears. This won't hurt at all!
7. You have a strong healthy heart.
8. I'm going to have to operate.
9. Please step over here to the X-ray machine.
10. Have a seat. What seems to be the problem?

Answers

1. nurse
2. hygienist
3. optometrist
4. dentist
5. obstetrician
6. pediatrician
7. cardiologist
8. surgeon
9. X-ray technician
10. psychiatrist

WORKBOOK PAGE 71

A. WHAT DID THE DOCTOR DO?

1. cast, sling
2. diet, exercise
3. prescription, rest
4. X-ray, crutches
5. stitches, bandaid

B. MATCHING: *WHAT DO THEY DO?*

1. d
2. a
3. b
4. e
5. c

C. WHICH WORD?

1. gown
2. diet
3. a prescription
4. control
5. physiotherapy
6. pan
7. medical chart
8. I.V.
9. fluids
10. shot

WORKBOOK PAGE 72

A. SOLUTIONS

1. lozenge
2. cough
3. vitamins
4. aspirins
5. ointment
6. antacid
7. decongestant spray
8. ointment
9. creme
10. aspirin

B. WHAT'S THE MEDICINE?

1. b
2. a
3. a
4. a
5. b
6. b
7. a

C. LISTENING: *WHAT'S THE DOSAGE?*
Listen to the directions. Circle the correct answer.

1. The doctor told me to take 3 teaspoons every 6 hours.
2. Every morning I take one tablet after breakfast.
3. She told me to take 2 teaspoons after every meal.
4. The dosage is 2 caplets every six hours.
5. You will take a tablet every day.
6. Take one capsule, every six hours.
7. The doctor said to take five capsules.
8. He told me to take seven caplets every night before bed.

Answers

1. 3 teaspoons
2. 1 tablet
3. 2 teaspoons
4. 2 caplets
5. 1 tablet
6. 1 capsule
7. 5 capsules
8. 7 caplets

WORKBOOK PAGE 73

A. SENDING MAIL

1. parcel
2. parcel post
3. of stamps
4. postcard
5. letter
6. postage
7. letter
8. post
9. envelope
10. machine
11. bag
12. change-of-address

B. WHICH WORD DOESN'T BELONG?

1. counter (The others appear on an envelope.)
2. mail truck (The others are people.)
3. mail bag (The others are classes of mail service.)
4. mail slot (The others are things to mail.)
5. scale (The others are things to mail.)
6. money order (The others are classes of mail service.)
7. postal clerk (The others appear on an envelope.)
8. express mail (The others are postal service property.)

C. MATCHING

1. registered mail
2. return address
3. first class
4. parcel post
5. letter carrier
6. postal code

WORKBOOK PAGE 74

A. AT THE LIBRARY

1. librarian
2. card catalogue
3. author
4. title
5. call number
6. shelves
7. magazines
8. periodicals
9. microfilm
10. library card
11. assistant
12. checkout desk

B. MATCHING: *LIBRARY HELP*

1. e
2. f
3. g
4. a
5. d
6. c
7. b

C. READING CALL CARDS

1. John A. Reynolds
2. 495
3. *Sports Around the World*
4. Sports
5. *The Importance of English*
6. 1991
7. *North American Short Stories*

WORKBOOK PAGE 75

A. AT SCHOOL

1. guidance counselor
2. teachers' lounge
3. cafeteria
4. locker
5. language lab
6. nurse
7. chemistry lab
8. track
9. teachers' lounge
10. field

B. MATCHING: *ASSOCIATIONS*

1. f
2. e
3. a
4. b
5. c
6. h
7. d
8. g

C. LISTENING: *WHO ARE THESE STUDENTS GOING TO SEE?*
Circle the correct word.

1. Attention, students. Sorry for the interruption. Would Jack Riley please report to the guidance counselor? Jack Riley—please report to the guidance counselor.
2. Please excuse the interruption. Would Cindy Bowman and Shirley Cross please meet Mr. Taylor for driver's education in the front parking lot?

3. Attention, all students and teachers. Mary Holmes and Janet Reed—please stop by the principal's office after school. Mary Holmes and Janet Reed to the principal's office after school. Thank you.
4. Attention, please. Sorry for the interruption. Johnny Brown. Johnny Brown. Please see Mrs. Wright for your eye examination.
5. Attention all students. All students willing to help clean the school grounds, report to Mr. Jackson in the basement after school. Thank you.
6. May I have your attention, please? George Walker—report to the cafeteria immediately.
7. Attention, please. All students interested in playing baseball, please meet in the gymnasium after school.
8. May I have your attention? Sorry for the interruption. Would Marla Jones please report to the office as soon as possible? Thank you.

Answers

1. guidance counselor
2. driver's ed instructor
3. principal
4. school nurse
5. caretaker
6. lunchroom monitor
7. coach
8. assistant principal

WORKBOOK PAGES 76-77

A. WHERE DO THESE SUBJECTS BELONG?

Mathematics:	Sciences:	Languages:
algebra	biology	Spanish
geometry	physics	English
calculus	chemistry	French
trigonometry		

B. MATCHING: ASSOCIATIONS

1. e
2. a
3. d
4. g
5. f
6. b
7. c

C. MATCHING: EXTRACURRICULAR ACTIVITIES

1. g
2. e
3. f
4. c
5. b
6. a
7. d

D. LISTENING: WHAT ARE THEY TALKING ABOUT?
Listen to the sentences and circle the correct words.

1. I'm not going to practise today. I have a sore throat. I can't sing!
2. We're having a meeting after school tomorrow. Bring the articles you wrote.
3. The test was easy! I understand angles very well.
4. I can drive well, but I have trouble parking!
5. Vamos a estudiar para el examen.
6. Six points! What a touchdown!
7. That was lovely. You played very well.
8. I like to learn about the past!

Answers

1. choir
2. school newspaper
3. geometry
4. driver's ed
5. Spanish
6. football
7. band
8. history

E. CROSSWORD (see p. 151)

WORKBOOK PAGES 78-79

A. WHAT'S THE WORD?

1. cashier
2. baker
3. actress
4. carpenter
5. architect
6. assembler
7. artist
8. bricklayer
9. bookkeeper
10. chef

B. MATCHING: WHAT DO THEY DO?

1. f
2. e
3. i
4. j
5. a
6. g
7. h
8. b
9. c
10. d

C. WHICH GROUP?

These people cut hair:	These people cook:
barber	chef
hairdresser	baker

These people clean:	These people deliver:
caretaker	courier
housekeeper	delivery person
	messenger

These people work with numbers and money:	These people build:
accountant	mason
bookkeeper	bricklayer
cashier	

D. MATCHING: COMPOUND WORDS

1. housekeeper
2. bookkeeper
3. bricklayer
4. firefighter
5. hairdresser

E. LISTENING: WHAT'S THE JOB?
Listen and circle the correct word.

1. I meet a lot of people every day. I know the streets of the city well.
2. Every day I cut beef, chicken, veal, and pork for my customers.
3. I like to write and do research. I use a word processor.
4. People call me when there's an emergency.
5. I cut people's hair every day.
6. I work outside. My job can be dangerous, so I often wear a helmet to protect my head.
7. I build things with wood. I use a hammer and nails.
8. I'm very good in math. I like to work with numbers.

Answers

1. bus driver
2. butcher
3. journalist
4. firefighter
5. barber
6. construction worker
7. carpenter
8. bookkeeper

F. CAREER EXPLORATION

1. accountant, bookkeeper
2. artist, assembler
3. bricklayer, construction worker, farmer, gardener
4. artist, architect, chef/cook
5. fisherman, delivery person, courier/messenger
6. actor/actress, barber, hairdresser, cashier

WORKBOOK PAGES 80-81

A. JOBS

1. mechanic
2. plumber
3. real estate agent
4. pharmacist
5. receptionist
6. photographer
7. newscaster
8. pilot
9. sanitation worker
10. police officer

B. MATCHING: WHERE DO THEY WORK?

1. d
2. f
3. a
4. b
5. g
6. c
7. e

C. MATCHING: *ASSOCIATIONS*

1. b	6. j
2. c	7. i
3. a	8. f
4. e	9. g
5. d	10. h

D. WHAT'S THE WORD?

1. painter	6. truck driver
2. interpreter	7. photographer
3. gardener	8. waiter
4. reporter	9. welder
5. farmer	

E. CROSSWORD (see p. 151)

WORKBOOK PAGES 82-83

A. MATCHING: *WHAT DO THEY DO?*

1. e	8. j
2. f	9. k
3. b	10. i
4. a	11. h
5. g	12. n
6. c	13. m
7. d	14. l

B. WHAT DO THEY DO?

1. paint	5. sew
2. fix things	6. teach
3. play an instrument	7. translate
4. serve food	8. type

C. WHAT'S THE WORK ACTIVITY?

draw   type   bake   assemble   grow

D. MATCHING: *ASSOCIATIONS*

1. e	7. h
2. d	8. i
3. b	9. l
4. c	10. k
5. f	11. g
6. a	12. j

E. MATCHING: *WHAT DOES IT MEAN?*

1. d	4. b
2. e	5. c
3. a	

F. LISTENING: *WHAT DO THEY DO?*
Listen and put a check next to the correct sentence.

1. I'm a security guard. I usually work at night.
2. I'm an assembler at a factory.
3. I grow vegetables and fruits and raise animals.
4. I play an instrument in a musical group. I work with other musicians.
5. I'm an architect.
6. I work as an English professor at a university.
7. I'm a secretary in an office.
8. I'm a seamstress. I make suits for men and women.
9. I'm a construction worker.

Answers

1. I guard buildings.	6. I teach.
2. I assemble components.	7. I type.
3. I'm a farmer.	8. I sew.
4. I play the piano.	9. I build things.
5. I design buildings.	

WORKBOOK PAGE 84

A. JOE'S DAILY ROUTINE

1. coat closet	5. coffee machine
2. mailbox	6. workstation
3. waste receptacle	7. typist
4. message board	

B. WHICH WORD?

1. employee lounge	6. office
2. boss	7. storage room
3. supply	8. workstations
4. mailbox	9. reception area
5. office manager	

C. MATCHING: *WHERE IS THIS CONVERSATION TAKING PLACE?*

1. e	4. b
2. c	5. a
3. d	

D. LISTENING: *WHO IS TALKING?*
Listen and circle the correct answer.

1. I filed all the reports.
2. Good afternoon. Have a seat. I'll tell Mr. Brown you're here.
3. My typewriter is broken.
4. Paycheques will be ready at 12 noon.
5. You're hired! When can you start working?
6. The boss isn't here right now. Can I take a message?

Answers

1. file clerk	4. administrative assistant
2. receptionist	5. boss
3. typist	6. secretary

WORKBOOK PAGE 85

A. WHAT'S THE WORD?

1. calculator
2. microcassette recorder
3. fax machine
4. plastic binding machine
5. phone system
6. paper shredder

B. WHICH WORD?

1. printer	4. system
2. processor	5. scale
3. shredder	6. cutter

C. MATCHING: *ASSOCIATIONS*

1. e	4. c
2. d	5. a
3. b	

D. LISTENING: *WHAT ARE THAY TALKING ABOUT?*
Listen and circle the correct words.Z

1. There's a problem with the fax machine.
2. Can I use your calculator?
3. Where's the paper cutter?
4. There's a problem with the dictaphone.
5. We need to get a new telex machine.
6. We need to fix the phone system.

Answers

1. fax machine	4. dictaphone
2. calculator	5. telex machine
3. paper cutter	6. phone system

WORKBOOK PAGE 86

A. WHICH GROUP?

Types of chairs:	Things we write with:	Things we write in or on:
clerical	highlighter	organizer
posture	mechanical pencil	appointment book
swivel		timesheet

B. MATCHING: *ASSOCIATIONS*

1. b	5. c
2. g	6. e
3. h	7. d
4. a	8. f

C. ANALOGIES

1. typewriter
2. pencils
3. highlighter pen
4. staple remover
5. stamp pad

D. WHICH WORD?

1. pencil
2. calendar
3. book
4. opener
5. cabinet
6. tray
7. dispenser
8. ink

WORKBOOK PAGE 87

A. WHICH WORD?

1. correction fluid
2. paper clip
3. note pad
4. mailing label
5. carbon paper
6. paper fasteners
7. rubber cement
8. stationery
9. mailing label
10. manila folder

B. WHICH WORD?

1. legal
2. plastic
3. computer
4. Post-It note
5. sealing
6. typing

C. MATCHING: *WHAT DO WE USE IT FOR?*

1. d
2. g
3. f
4. e
5. a
6. b
7. h
8. i
9. c

WORKBOOK PAGE 88

D. LISTENING: *TAKING A MESSAGE*
Listen to the telephone conversations. Write the messages.

1. A. Could I speak to Mr. Taylor, please?
   B. Mr. Taylor isn't here right now. Would you like to leave a message?
   A. Yes, thank you. This is Mrs. Perez. Could you ask him to call me at (905) 986-3098?
   B. Certainly. That's (905) 986-3098.
   A. That's correct. And my name is Mrs. Perez. P-E-R-E-Z. Please ask him to call back today.
   B. All right. I'll give him the message.

2. A. This is Mr. White. I'd like to speak to Mr. Franco.
   B. Mr. Franco isn't here right now. Would you like to leave a message?
   A. Yes, thank you. Could you have him call me at (604) 554-8984?
   B. Yes. That's Mr. White at (604) 554-8984, right?
   A. Yes. And please tell him to call before 5:00.

3. A. May I speak to Mrs. Donna Ling? This is her husband, Mr. Ling.
   B. Mrs. Ling isn't here right now. Would you like to leave a message?
   A. Yes, please. She needs to call me immediately at (403) 354-3963.
   B. Is this urgent?
   A. Yes, it is.
   B. All right. And the number again is (403) 354-3963. Is that correct?
   A. Yes. That's correct. Thank you.

4. A. I'm returning Ms. Benson's phone call. This is Mrs. Hobbs.
   B. Ms. Benson isn't here right now. Could I take a message?
   A. No, that's okay. I'll call again. Just tell her I have some important news.
   B. All right.

Answers

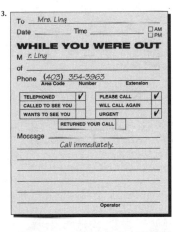

1. To _Mr. Taylor_
   Date _____ Time _____ ☐ AM ☐ PM
   WHILE YOU WERE OUT
   M _rs. Perez_
   of _____
   Phone (_905_) _986-3098_
   Area Code Number Extension
TELEPHONED	✓	PLEASE CALL	✓
CALLED TO SEE YOU		WILL CALL AGAIN	
WANTS TO SEE YOU		URGENT	
	RETURNED YOUR CALL		
   Message _____ _Call back today._ _____
   Operator

2. To _Mr. Franco_
   Date _____ Time _____ ☐ AM ☐ PM
   WHILE YOU WERE OUT
   M _r. White_
   of _____
   Phone (_604_) _554-8984_
   Area Code Number Extension
TELEPHONED	✓	PLEASE CALL	✓
CALLED TO SEE YOU		WILL CALL AGAIN	
WANTS TO SEE YOU		URGENT	
	RETURNED YOUR CALL		
   Message _____ _Call before 5:00._
   Operator

3. To _Mrs. Ling_
   Date _____ Time _____ ☐ AM ☐ PM
   WHILE YOU WERE OUT
   M _r. Ling_
   of _____
   Phone (_403_) _354-3963_
   Area Code Number Extension
TELEPHONED	✓	PLEASE CALL	✓
CALLED TO SEE YOU		WILL CALL AGAIN	
WANTS TO SEE YOU		URGENT	✓
	RETURNED YOUR CALL		
   Message _____ _Call immediately._
   Operator

4. To _Ms. Benson_
   Date _____ Time _____ ☐ AM ☐ PM
   WHILE YOU WERE OUT
   M _rs. Hobbs_
   of _____
   Phone ( )
   Area Code Number Extension
TELEPHONED		PLEASE CALL	
CALLED TO SEE YOU		WILL CALL AGAIN	✓
WANTS TO SEE YOU		URGENT	
	RETURNED YOUR CALL	✓	
   Message _____ _She has some important news._
   Operator

WORKBOOK PAGE 89

A. WHICH WORD?

1. fire extinguisher
2. vending machine
3. forklift
4. first-aid kit
5. payroll office
6. supply room
7. personnel office
8. foreman
9. card
10. suggestion box

B. MATCHING: *FINISH THE WORDS*

1. c
2. e
3. b
4. a
5. d
6. i
7. h
8. j
9. g
10. f

C. WHICH WORD?

1. machine
2. elevator
3. department
4. dock
5. office

D. MATCHING: *DEFINITIONS*

1. c
2. d
3. f
4. a
5. e
6. g
7. b

WORKBOOK PAGE 90

A. WHICH GROUP?

Vehicles:	Tools:	Building materials:
bulldozer	pickax	brick
pickup truck	shovel	cement
crane	jackhammer	plywood
van	sledgehammer	lumber

B. WHICH WORD?

1. wheelbarrow
2. helmet
3. plywood
4. trowel
5. blueprints
6. ladder
7. shingles
8. bulldozer

C. MATCHING: *COMPOUND WORDS*

1. backhoe
2. blueprints
3. bulldozer
4. pickax
5. sledgehammer
6. toolbelt
7. wheelbarrow

D. LISTENING: *WHAT ARE THEY TALKING ABOUT?*
Listen and circle the correct word.

1. The construction workers will bring the beam in the pickup truck.
2. Could you get me that trowel?
3. Let me show you how to start the van.
4. We need the blueprints as soon as possible.
5. Watch out for that backhoe!
6. They should use a level there.
7. Take the girder over there.
8. Can you pick up that shingle and bring it here?
9. Do you know how to operate a front-end loader?
10. Could I borrow your tape measure?
11. I can't find the hardhats!
12. I'll get more wire from the supply room.

Answers

1. beam
2. trowel
3. van
4. blueprints
5. backhoe
6. level
7. girder
8. shingle
9. front-end loader
10. tape measure
11. hardhats
12. wire

WORKBOOK PAGE 91

A. MATCHING: *WHAT SHOULD THEY USE?*

1. h
2. g
3. a
4. e
5. c
6. d
7. b
8. f

B. MATCHING: *COMPOUND WORDS*

1. tailpipe
2. headlight
3. hubcap
4. sunroof
5. dashboard
6. dipstick
7. windshield

C. WHICH WORD?

1. signal
2. mirror
3. plate
4. belt
5. tire
6. wipers
7. dipstick
8. seat belt

D. WHICH WORD?

1. visor
2. horn
3. ignition
4. stickshift
5. glove compartment
6. tow truck

E. MATCHING: *ASSOCIATIONS*

1. d
2. c
3. b
4. a
5. f
6. h
7. e
8. g
9. j
10. i

F. SAFETY FIRST

1. trunk
2. jumper cables
3. flares
4. jack
5. spare tire
6. seat belts
7. air bags

G. LISTENING: *CHECKLIST*
Listen to the car dealers. Put a check next to the items each car has.

1. A. This is a very nice car.
   B. I like the sunroof. Does this car come with a luggage carrier?
   A. No, it doesn't. But it has a very large trunk.
   B. I'd like to look in the trunk. Oh, good. . . There's a jack and a spare tire, of course. I notice there isn't a side mirror.
   A. A side mirror is extra on this car. I can get one for you for about $100. Did I tell you about the cruise control?
   B. Yes, you did.
   A. And the rear defroster?
   B. Yes, you did. Does this car have an air bag?
   A. No, it doesn't. But it has a nice tape deck.
2. A. I'm interested in this car.
   B. Yes, ma'am. Now please understand. This car is our cheapest model. It doesn't have a lot of features. It doesn't have a sunroof or a luggage carrier.
   A. I understand. Is there a jack and a spare tire?
   B. Yes, of course. But there isn't a side mirror or cruise control.
   A. Rear defroster?
   B. Yes, ma'am. There is a rear defroster.
   A. Air bag?
   B. I'm afraid not in this model.
   A. Is there a tape deck?
   B. No, ma'am. There's a radio, but we can install a tape deck, if you want.

Answers

✓ sunroof	__ sunroof
__ luggage carrier	__ luggage carrier
✓ jack	✓ jack
✓ spare tire	✓ spare tire
__ side mirror	__ side mirror
✓ cruise control	__ cruise control
✓ rear defroster	✓ rear defroster
__ air bag	__ air bag
✓ tape deck	__ tape deck

WORKBOOK PAGE 93

A. WHICH WORD?
1. stop
2. exit
3. intersection
4. speed limit
5. crosswalk
6. service area
7. snowplough
8. corner

B. MATCHING: *ASSOCIATIONS*
1. f
2. a
3. e
4. d
5. c
6. b

C. WHAT ARE THEY TALKING ABOUT?
1. school crossing
2. service area
3. yield sign
4. snowplough
5. speed limit sign
6. tunnel

E. LISTENING: *TRAFFIC SIGNS*
Listen to the conversations. Write the number under the correct sign.
1. Careful! You can't make a left turn here!
2. Oh, you can't go there. It says, "Do not enter."
3. Didn't you see that sign? You were supposed to stop.
4. See that sign? You can't turn here.
5. You can't turn right here.

Answers
2   4   1   3   5

WORKBOOK PAGE 94

A. WHERE DID THEY GO?
1. train station
2. information booth
3. timetable
4. train
5. ticket window
6. arrival and departure board
7. track
8. porter
9. luggage
10. platform

B. WHICH WORD DOESN'T BELONG?
1. turnstile (The others are people.)
2. token (The others are people.)
3. sleeper (The others are used to pay a fare.)
4. engine (The others are places passengers wait.)
5. porter (The others are types of rail cars.)
6. transfer (The others are people.)

C. WHICH WORD?
1. sleeper
2. fare
3. platform
4. bus station
5. timetable
6. token
7. porter
8. counter

D. WHERE ARE THEY?
Listen to the conversations and decide where the passengers are.
1. Can I please have a transfer?
2. Buy your token. Then put it in the turnstile.
3. Can you recommend a hotel near here?
4. The porter is taking your luggage to your sleeper.
5. The food smells good!
6. The meter says you own me 15 dollars, sir.

Answers
4   2   5
6   1   3

WORKBOOK PAGE 95

A. WHICH WORD?
1. check-in counter
2. suitcase
3. metal detector
4. boarding pass
5. waiting area
6. porter
7. declaration form
8. garment bag

B. WHICH WORD DOESN'T BELONG?
1. luggage carrier (The others are people.)
2. immigration (The others refer to baggage.)
3. X-ray machine (The others are paper.)
4. baggage carousel (The others relate to security.)
5. immigration (The others are in passenger waiting areas.)
6. gate (The others are documents.)

C. A TICKET
1. James Johnson
2. Air Canada
3. July 5
4. 5:05 P.M.
5. Toronto
6. Madrid
7. 723
8. $804.00
9. May 12

WORKBOOK PAGE 96

A. WHAT DO THEY NEED?
1. air sickness bag
2. seat control
3. lavatory
4. overhead compartment
5. oxygen mask
6. galley

B. WHICH WORD?
1. panel
2. belt
3. exit
4. building
5. gear
6. nose

C. MATCHING: *WHAT IS IT?*
1. d
2. f
3. e
4. a
5. g
6. c
7. h
8. b

D. LISTENING
Listen and check the words you hear.
1. Good morning, ladies and gentlemen and welcome to flight 304 to Montreal. This is your flight attendant, Sally. Let me go over a few safety suggestions. In case of an emergency, the oxygen mask will appear from above your seat. Pull the mask over your nose and mouth and breathe normally. Please take a minute to look at the emergency instruction card located in the seat pocket in front of you. You will find emergency exits on both sides of the cabin. Now, if you will fasten your seat belt, we are about to take off. We will begin serving your meal about 30 minutes after takeoff.
2. Good evening, passengers. This is your co-pilot, Captain Jack Martino. Welcome to Flight 734 to Winnipeg. You'll notice the Fasten Seat Belt sign is on. We'll be on the runway for about 3 minutes, and then we'll take off. On behalf of your pilot and flight attendants, I hope you enjoy this evening's flight.
3. Ladies and gentlemen, we'll be landing at London's Heathrow Airport in about 15 minutes. Please fasten your seat belts and observe the No Smoking sign. Please put your trays up and put any bags under the seat in front of you. Please remain in your seats until the airplane taxis to the terminal building and comes to a complete stop.

Answers

1. ✓ seat belt
   __ bathroom
   __ life vest
   __ call button
   ✓ oxygen mask
   ✓ emergency exit
   ✓ meal
   ✓ emergency
      instruction card

2. ✓ co-pilot
   __ flight engineer
   ✓ flight attendants
   __ window seat
   ✓ Fasten Seat Belt sign
   __ meal
   ✓ runway
   __ control tower

3. ✓ tray
   __ oxygen mask
   ✓ seat belt
   __ seat control
   __ landing gear
   __ runway
   ✓ terminal building
   ✓ No Smoking sign

WORKBOOK PAGE 97

A. WHAT'S THE WORD?

1. raining
2. foggy
3. snowing
4. clear
5. windy

B. MATCHING: *ASSOCIATIONS*

1. c
2. a
3. d
4. b
5. g
6. e
7. h
8. f

C. FAHRENHEIT AND CELSIUS

1. a
2. b
3. a
4. a
5. b
6. a

D. LISTENING: *WEATHER FORECASTS*
Listen and write the number under the correct picture.

1. Good morning. It's going to be hot and muggy today. In fact, it will reach 30 degrees Celsius by this afternoon. It will cool off this evening with an eighty percent chance of a thunderstorm.
2. Tomorrow's forecast looks like this: We can expect that snowstorm to arrive early in the morning. Snow will accumulate two to four inches. Temperatures will drop to minus 5 degrees Celsius.
3. The forecast for the next few days looks like this: cool in the mornings, but warm, sunny afternoons. An April drizzle will help those buds blossom into flowers.
4. For the next few days, we'll have warm sunny days and cool, clear evenings—perfect weather to watch the leaves turn colour!

Answers

1   4   3   2

WORKBOOK PAGE 98

A. WHICH WORD?

1. bag
2. basket
3. stakes
4. trail map
5. lantern
6. thermos
7. backpack
8. rope

B. MATCHING

1. b
2. d
3. a
4. c
5. g
6. h
7. f
8. e

C. MATCHING

1. d
2. c
3. f
4. e
5. b
6. a

D. LISTENING: *WHERE ARE THEY GOING?*
Listen and write the number next to the correct word.

1. A. Great idea! Let's go this weekend!
   B. I have one problem. I don't have a harness.
   A. That's not a problem. I have a rope and harness you can use.
2. A. Let's go under those trees!
   B. But there isn't a table.
   A. That's okay. I brought a blanket to sit on.
   B. Okay. Let's see what's in the basket. I'm hungry!
3. A. Which way do we go now?
   B. I don't know. Let's look at the trail map.
4. A. Here are the sleeping bags. Where is the tent? In your backpack?
   B. No. Let's sleep under the stars tonight!

Answers

4   3   1   2

WORKBOOK PAGE 99

A. WHICH WORD?

1. water fountain
2. at the zoo
3. in the bike rack
4. jogging path
5. trash can
6. bridle path
7. band shell
8. grill

B. ANALOGIES

1. sandbox
2. bridle path
3. duck pond
4. washroom
5. jogging path
6. tire swing

C. WHAT ARE THEY TALKING ABOUT?

1. jungle gym
2. duck pond
3. water fountain
4. seesaw
5. bench
6. picnic area
7. zoo
8. statue

D. LISTENING: *WHAT ARE THEY TALKING ABOUT?*
Listen and circle the correct word.

1. Don't go so high! Be careful! You'll fall!
2. It's closed. We can't get in!
3. There are swings and a slide!
4. Let's go over there. There are tables and a grill.
5. The children really enjoy playing in it!
6. Have a drink! The water's cold!
7. Please throw this away for me.
8. Can we please ride on it?

Answers

1. jungle gym
2. washroom
3. playground
4. picnic area
5. sandbox
6. fountain
7. trash can
8. carousel

WORKBOOK PAGE 100

A. MATCHING: *WHAT DO THEY DO?*

1. c
2. d
3. a
4. b
5. f
6. h
7. e
8. g

B. WHICH WORD?

1. beach umbrella
2. sunglasses
3. kite
4. blanket
5. refreshment stand
6. beach ball
7. swimsuit
8. bucket
9. swimmer
10. waves

C. ANALOGIES

1. bathing cap
2. swimsuit
3. kite
4. lifeguard stand
5. raft
6. wave

D. LISTENING: *WHAT ARE THEY TALKING ABOUT?*

Listen and circle the correct word.

1. Would you like to sit down?
2. There's no air in it!
3. Put this on and your hair won't get wet.
4. Here. Use this to dry off.
5. Put this on. You won't get a sunburn.
6. Just a minute. I have to get my surfboard.
7. I'll put this down and we can sit on it.
8. Do you have one for me?

Answers

1. chair
2. raft
3. bathing cap
4. towel
5. sunscreen
6. surfer
7. blanket
8. life preserver

WORKBOOK PAGE 101

A. WHAT ARE THEY?

Things you throw:
darts
frisbee

Things you wear on your feet:
bowling shoes
jogging shoes
walking shoes

Things you wear on your hands:
handball glove
boxing gloves

B. MATCHING: *ASSOCIATIONS*

1. d
2. c
3. b
4. a
5. f
6. g
7. e

C. WHICH WORD?

1. stirrups
2. helmet
3. safety goggles
4. frisbee
5. weights
6. trampoline
7. stick
8. arrow
9. uniform
10. handball

D. ANALOGIES

1. paddle
2. golf club
3. roller skating
4. archery
5. skydiving
6. billiard balls

WORKBOOK PAGE 102

A. WHICH SPORTS?

1. baseball, softball, football, lacrosse, hockey
2. football
3. baseball, softball, football, lacrosse, soccer
4. hockey

B. CROSSWORD (see p. 152)

WORKBOOK PAGE 103

A. MATCHING: *ASSOCIATIONS*

1. e
2. g
3. a
4. d
5. h
6. c
7. b
8. f

B. WHICH WORD?

1. helmet
2. mask
3. stick
4. hoop
5. helmets
6. glove
7. hockey
8. uniforms

C. WHICH WORD DOESN'T BELONG?

1. shinguard (The others are worn on the head.)
2. bat (The others are items hit during the game.)
3. backboard (The others are used for hitting.)
4. shoulder pads (The others are worn on the hand.)
5. hockey (The others are played on a field or court, not on ice.)

D. LISTENING: *WHICH SPORT IS IT?*

Listen to the radio announcer and write the number next to the correct picture.

1. Nice pass! He's going toward the basket. He misses! He gets the rebound. It's in!!
2. The ball is hit into left field. The left fielder is running. He catches it. Oh! The ball falls out of his glove!
3. He's got the ball. But oh no! He drops the stick!
4. Good pass. He slams the puck! Goal!
5. It's a long pass! He caught it! He caught it! He's going for a touchdown!
6. He kicks. It's a goal!

Answers

2	5	3
4	1	6

WORKBOOK PAGE 104

A. WHICH SPORTS?

1. downhill skiing, cross-country skiing
2. ice skating, figure skating
3. snowmobiling
4. sledding, bobsledding, snowmobiling, tobogganing

B. MATCHING: *WHERE?*

1. c
2. d
3. a
4. e
5. b

C. WHICH WORD?

1. poles
2. skating
3. snowmobile
4. bobsledding
5. toboggan
6. Cross-country

D. MATCHING: *DEFINITIONS*

1. b
2. d
3. a
4. e
5. c

WORKBOOK PAGE 105

A. WHICH WORD?

1. surfboard
2. waterskiing
3. fishing
4. mask
5. fishing
6. sailing

B. MATCHING: *ASSOCIATIONS*

1. d
2. e
3. a
4. b
5. c

C. ANALOGIES

1. paddles
2. sailboard
3. wet suit
4. flippers
5. air tank
6. swimsuit

D. LISTENING: *WHAT ARE THEY DOING?*
Listen and write the number under the correct picture.
1. A. I brought my bathing suit and towel.
   B. Great! Let's go to the pool.
2. A. The ocean looks calm.
   B. I think the waves are big enough.
3. A. I got one!
   B. Look how big it is!
4. A. Here's the towrope.
   B. Thanks. I'm ready. Start the boat!
5. A. Can you show me how to use these?
   B. You don't know how to use paddles?
6. A. Is this your first time?
   B. Yes. It's fun to use the snorkel and flippers.

Answers

5	2	3
1	4	6

WORKBOOK PAGE 106

A. WHICH WORD?
1. bend
2. pass
3. Dribble
4. Dive
5. Shoot
6. run
7. stretch
8. Swing
9. Hit
10. Hop

B. ANALOGIES
1. shoot
2. throw
3. baseball
4. hands
5. hop
6. kneel

C. MATCHING: *ASSOCIATIONS*
1. e
2. d
3. b
4. c
5. a

D. LISTENING: *AEROBICS*
Listen and put the number under the correct picture.
1. Okay, everybody! I want you to stretch. Stretch those muscles. Stretch, stretch!
2. Now reach to the ceiling! As high as you can. Reach, reach!
3. Okay, now bend. Bend to the floor. . . bend, bend.
4. Now swing those arms. To the left, to the right. Swing, swing.
5. Okay. Now I want you to jump in place. Up and down, up and down. Jump, jump!
6. Now one foot at a time. Hop, left. Hop, right. Hop, hop.

Answers

5	2	3	1	6	4

WORKBOOK PAGE 107

A. WHAT'S THE WORD?
1. woodworking
2. photography
3. sewing
4. painting
5. astronomy
6. games
7. pottery
8. coin collecting

B. MATCHING: *ASSOCIATIONS*
1. c
2. e
3. a
4. d
5. b

C. ANALOGIES
1. coin album
2. knitting
3. knitting needle
4. bird watching
5. binoculars

D. WHAT ARE THEY TALKING ABOUT?
1. coin collecting
2. astronomy
3. sewing
4. bird watching
5. Scrabble

WORKBOOK PAGE 108

A. WHICH WORD?
1. audience
2. spotlight
3. lobby
4. balcony
5. company
6. tickets
7. chorus
8. baton

B. MATCHING
1. d
2. c
3. b
4. e
5. a

C. WHICH WORD DOESN'T BELONG?
1. usher (The others are places in a theatre.)
2. billboard (The others are people.)
3. toeshoes (The others are people.)
4. ballerina (The others are groups of people, not individuals.)
5. ticket (The others are places in a theatre.)
6. conductor (The others are dancers.)

D. WHO IS TALKING?
1. musician
2. usher
3. ballerina
4. actress
5. conductor

WORKBOOK PAGE 109

A. WHO LIKES WHAT?
1. music
2. play
3. TV programs
4. movies

B. LISTENING: *WHAT KIND OF MUSIC?*
Listen and circle the correct words.
1. I really like classical music.
2. I love bluegrass!
3. I really like reggae.
4. Do you like rap music?

Answers
1. classical music
2. bluegrass
3. reggae
4. rap music

C. WHAT TYPE OF MOVIE IS IT?
1. cartoon
2. western
3. war
4. foreign
5. comedy

D. WHAT TYPE OF TV PROGRAM IS IT?
1. talk show
2. game show
3. children's show
4. news program
5. music video
6. sports show

WORKBOOK PAGE 110

A. WHICH WORD DOESN'T BELONG?
1. banjo (The others are keyboard instruments.)
2. accordion (The others are string instruments.)
3. trumpet (The others are woodwinds.)
4. clarinet (The others are string instruments.)
5. harmonica (The others are percussion instruments.)

B. CROSSWORD (see p. 152)

B. CROSSWORD (see p. 152)

C. LISTENING: *WHICH INSTRUMENT IS IT?*
1. It's my favourite string instrument.
2. It's my favourite woodwind instrument.
3. It's my favourite brass instrument.
4. It's my favourite percussion instrument.
5. It's my favourite keyboard instrument.
6. It's my favourite instrument in a rock band.

Answers
1. viola
2. clarinet
3. trumpet
4. xylophone
5. synthesizer
6. electric guitar

WORKBOOK PAGE 111

A. WHAT'S THE WORD?
1. leaves
2. branch
3. grass
4. maple
5. tulips
6. palm

B. MATCHING: *ASSOCIATIONS*
1. b
2. d
3. a
4. e
5. c

C. ANALOGIES
1. trunk
2. flower
3. cactus
4. bulb
5. sunflower

D. CROSSWORD (see p. 153)

WORKBOOK PAGE 112

A. WHICH WORD?
1. river
2. forest
3. oil
4. valley
5. brook
6. hill
7. toxic waste
8. cliff

B. WHICH WORD DOESN'T BELONG?
1. desert (The others relate to water.)
2. rapids (The others relate to land.)
3. bay (The others are energy sources.)
4. ocean (The others relate to land.)
5. hill (The others relate to water.)
6. solar energy (The others relate to environmental problems.)
7. seashore (The others relate to areas of land with dense vegetation and trees.)

C. MATCHING: *WHAT'S THE PLACE?*
1. b
2. d
3. a
4. c
5. e

D. MATCHING: *ASSOCIATIONS*
1. d
2. e
3. c
4. b
5. a

WORKBOOK PAGE 113

A. WHICH WORD?
1. hay
2. garden
3. scarecrow
4. irrigation system
5. pitchfork
6. barnyard
7. sheep
8. barn

B. ANALOGIES
1. hen
2. horse
3. goat
4. chicken
5. farmer
6. piglet
7. calf

C. MATCHING: *ASSOCIATIONS*
1. e
2. a
3. b
4. f
5. c
6. h
7. d
8. g

D. MATCHING
1. b
2. d
3. a
4. c
5. f
6. e

WORKBOOK PAGES 114-115

A. WHICH WORD?
1. kitten
2. stripes
3. gerbil
4. llama
5. pony
6. squirrel
7. monkeys
8. puppy

B. MATCHING: *WHICH ANIMAL IS IT?*
1. e
2. b
3. f
4. c
5. a
6. d
7. l
8. k
9. g
10. h
11. j
12. i

C. ANALOGIES
1. foal
2. rhinoceros
3. mouse
4. zebra
5. lion
6. beaver
7. dog
8. quills
9. gibbon
10. wolf

D. WHICH WORD DOESN'T BELONG?
1. raccoon (The others relate to horses.)
2. wolves (The others are rodents.)
3. buffalo (The others are parts that grow on certain animals.)
4. pouch (The others are external parts of animals.)
5. gorilla (The others are types of bears.)
6. mouse (The others are young animals.)
7. dog (The others are rodents.)

E. MATCHING: *WHAT DO THEY EAT?*
1. b
2. f
3. e
4. c
5. h
6. a
7. d
8. g

F. LISTENING: *WHAT ANIMAL IS IT?*
Listen and circle the correct word.
1. She wasn't happy to see a bat yesterday.
2. We heard a moose last night.
3. We saw a lion at the zoo last week.
4. What a big raccoon!
5. Look at that hyena!
6. Do you see the fawn?
7. Look at the donkey!
8. The anteater is a very interesting animal.
9. We went to the zoo and saw a koala bear.
10. Is that a leopard?

Answers
1. bat
2. moose
3. lion
4. raccoon
5. hyena
6. fawn
7. donkey
8. anteater
9. koala bear
10. leopard

G. MAKING COMPARISONS
1. bear
2. fox
3. donkey
4. pig
5. bull
6. cow
7. mouse
8. owl
9. bat
10. beaver

H. LISTENING: *WHICH ANIMAL IS IT?*
Listen and circle the correct word.
1. This animal has quills.
2. This animal has antlers.
3. This animal has a hump.
4. This animal has a trunk.
5. This animal has stripes.
6. This animal has a mane.

Answers
1. porcupine
2. moose
3. camel
4. elephant
5. zebra
6. lion

WORKBOOK PAGE 116

A. WHICH BIRD?
1. owl
2. hummingbird
3. pigeon
4. parrot
5. penguin
6. peacock
7. eagle

B. WHICH INSECT?
1. spider
2. firefly
3. flea
4. caterpillar
5. termite
6. tick
7. bee
8. cricket

C. ANALOGIES
1. nest
2. bill
3. cockroach
4. web
5. woodpecker
6. feather

D. LISTENING: *WHICH BIRD OR INSECT?*
Listen and circle the correct answer.
1. It has a beak.
2. It has claws.
3. It has a bill.
4. It spins a web.
5. It's my favourite bird.
6. What kind of insect is this?

Answers
1. woodpecker
2. eagle
3. duck
4. spider
5. cockatoo
6. scorpion

WORKBOOK PAGE 117

A. MATCHING: *ASSOCIATIONS*
1. b
2. c
3. e
4. f
5. a
6. d

B. ANALOGIES
1. snake
2. lizard
3. alligator
4. claw
5. mussels
6. starfish
7. seal

C. WHICH WORD DOESN'T BELONG?
1. seal (The others are parts of fish.)
2. walrus (The others are snakes.)
3. whale (The others are shellfish.)
4. flounder (The others are sea animals.)
5. eel (The others are sea animals.)
6. crab (The others are large.)
7. iguana (The others live in water.)
8. tadpole (The others are parts of animals.)

WORKBOOK PAGE 118

A. WHICH HAS THE SAME MEANING?
1. b
2. d
3. e
4. c
5. a

B. ANALOGIES
1. depth
2. metre
3. square
4. triangle
5. ellipse
6. diameter
7. wide

C. MATCHING: *ABBREVIATIONS*
1. c
2. g
3. a
4. b
5. d
6. e
7. f

D. WHAT DOES IT EQUAL?
1. mile
2. inch
3. yard
4. foot

WORKBOOK PAGE 119

A. DO YOU REMEMBER?

Mercury	Mars	Uranus
Venus	Jupiter	Neptune
Earth	Saturn	Pluto

B. MATCHING
1. d
2. c
3. a
4. e
5. b

C. CROSSWORD: *PICTURES TO WORDS* (see p. 153)

B. CROSSWORD: *PICTURES AND WORDS*

C. CROSSWORD: *WHAT DO WE DO?*

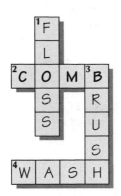

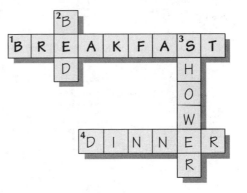

WORKBOOK PAGE 12

C. CROSSWORD

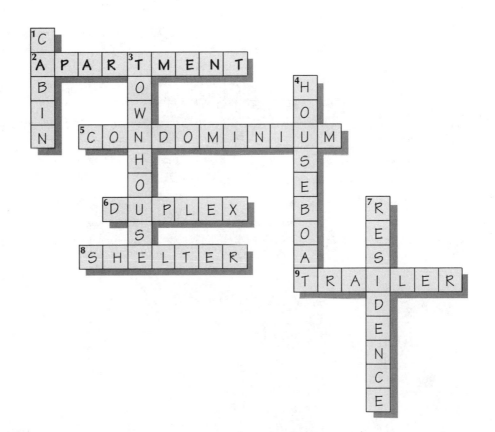

WORKBOOK PAGE 17

D. CROSSWORD

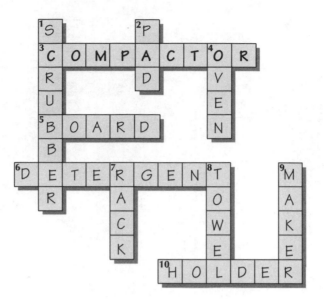

WORKBOOK PAGE 20

C. CROSSWORD: *PICTURES TO WORDS*

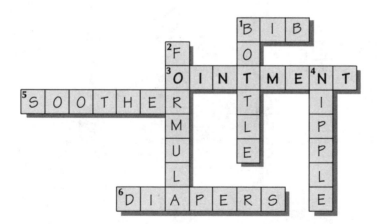

WORKBOOK PAGE 24

C. CROSSWORD

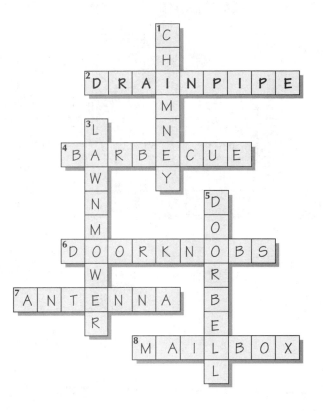

WORKBOOK PAGE 30

C. CROSSWORD: *NUMBERS TO WORDS*

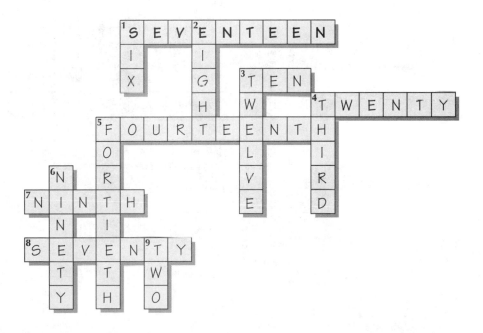

WORKBOOK PAGE 35

C. CROSSWORD: *PICTURES TO WORDS*

WORKBOOK PAGES 39

D. CROSSWORD: *OPPOSITES*

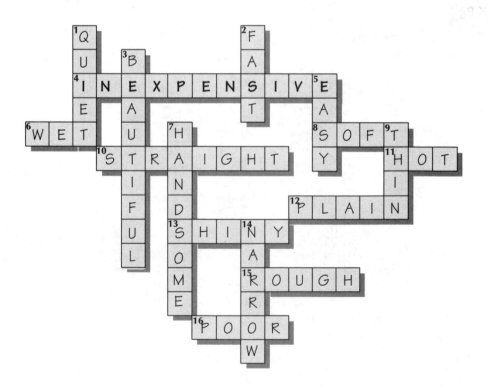

WORKBOOK PAGE 41

C. CROSSWORD: *PICTURES TO WORDS*

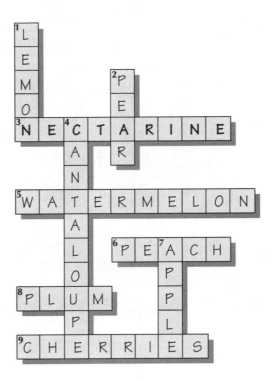

WORKBOOK PAGE 42

C. CROSSWORD: *PICTURES TO WORDS*

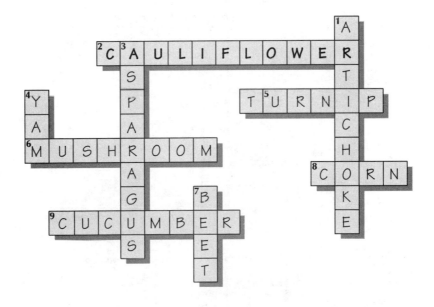

D. CROSSWORD: *PICTURES TO WORDS*

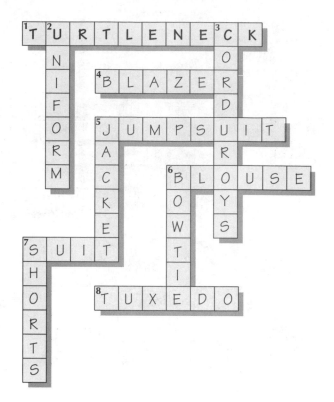

WORKBOOK PAGES 69

E. CROSSWORD

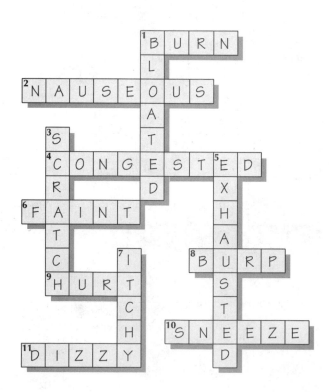

WORKBOOK PAGES 77

E. CROSSWORD

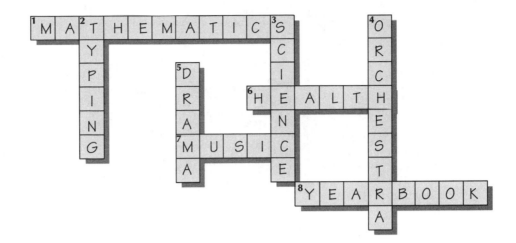

WORKBOOK PAGES 81

E. CROSSWORD

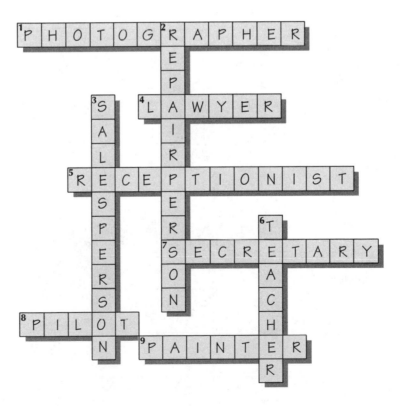

WORKBOOK PAGE 102

B. CROSSWORD

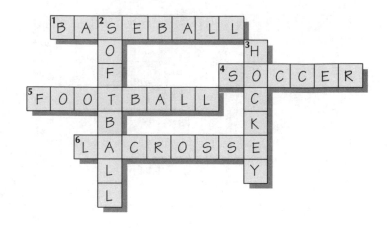

WORKBOOK PAGE 110

B. CROSSWORD

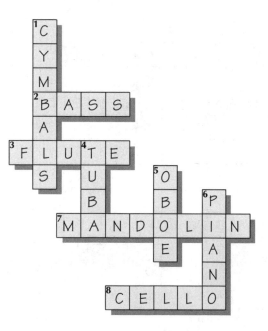

B. CROSSWORD

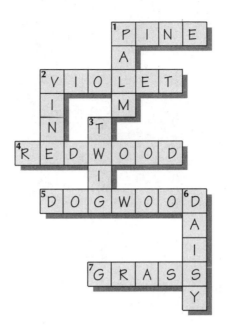

C. CROSSWORD: *PICTURES TO WORDS*

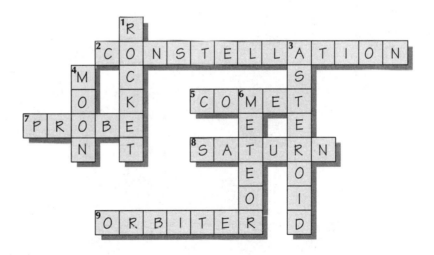